16.99

ER 4/90

MW00584087

A FIELD GUIDE TO
AUSTRALIAN OPALS

A FIELD GUIDE TO
AUSTRALIAN
OPALS

BARRIE O'LEARY

GEMCRAFT

Dedicated to all lapidary clubs
and gem societies everywhere

National Library of Australia
Cataloguing-in-Publication entry

O'Leary, Barrie.
  Field guide to Australian opals.
  Index
  ISBN 0 7270 0387 9.
  1. Opals—Australia. I. Title.

553.87

GEMCRAFT PUBLICATIONS PTY. LTD.
291-293 Wattletree Road,
East Malvern, Vic. 3145
Phone (03) 509 1611

First published in 1977
by Rigby Limited.

Second edition 1984
by Gemcraft Publications Pty. Ltd.

CONTENTS

ACKNOWLEDGMENTS

The author gratefully acknowledges the assistance he has had in preparing the illustrative material in this publication from the following firms and people.

For making opals available to photograph: E. Gregory Sherman Pty Ltd, Totterdell Jewellers, Percy Marks Pty Ltd, Superior Opal Traders, Mayneside Industries Pty Ltd, E. & F. Holdings, Australian Opal Distributors Pty Ltd, Gemtec Australia Pty Ltd, and Mrs I. Piggott.

For permission to reproduce certain illustrations: Mr R. Ball, University of New South Wales, for the black and white photographs of opal microstructures; Dr A. Kalokerinos for the slide showing hexagonal harlequin pattern; Dr B. Senior, Bureau of Mineral Resources, Canberra, for the slides showing Queensland boulder opal and Yowah nut band in situ; and Mayneside Industries Pty Ltd, Botany, New South Wales.

For the superb cartography: Mr L. Hay.

For the lucid microstructure illustration: Mr R. O'Leary.

FOREWORD

I have thoroughly researched all aspects of the subject of opal, and from this work conclude that here in Australia there are 500 000 square kilometres of Cretaceous sediments in which precious opals can occur. Top quality precious opal is so valuable that $100 million worth of it could be spread over a dinner table and most of the table would show through. This raises the fascinating possibility that Australia may have the most extensive and valuable mineral deposit in the whole world.

It is possible to foresee that long after all other precious stone deposits become depleted, the opal country of inland Australia will continue to yield a supply of natural precious stones. Opal certainly does have a future.

This fabulous treasure is being left to the efforts of gougers, most of whom are prepared to put in great effort and much time in pursuit of the gem, but who are not aware of the advantages science can offer them. Opal has to be mined economically and at a profit, and this can be done. How? By using geology in conjunction with knowledge of the way gem opal is formed to determine, before any holes are sunk and drives extended, which is the most promising ground.

Today the opal trade is big business, but there exists an appalling lack of product knowledge. The gouger is after opal and the dealer needs to buy it. The dealer, if he is to survive, must establish a reliable source of supply. And the gouger, if he is to carry on, must find payable opal continuously. Both need the high grade opal which is not being found these days! It is therefore all the more unfortunate that so little has been done to explain opal to the enthusiastic mineral collector, the professional jeweller, the opal dealer, or the general public.

This is a condensed work on Australian opal. It is meant to be read for interest, but there are comprehensive sections on how to classify opal patterns and establish relative values. It also lists all locations where opal has been discovered in Australia. My hope is that this book will guide you to a better understanding of opal, and that you will discover what a fascinating mineral our opal really is.

OPALS OF AUSTRALIA

There are many aspects to the fifth precious stone, opal. Lamentably, the Australian opal industry is unaware of the numerous vignettes of folklore associated with this gemstone, but more unfortunately a workable classification of opal has not been compiled until now. Here then are the facts, combined into one specialised manual on opal, and in particular, Australian opal.

The word *opal* is an ideal starting topic for consideration. Most mineralogical texts say that it is derived from the Sanskrit *upala*, meaning 'a precious stone.' A tame rendition actually! Opal was introduced into Greece during the first century B.C. The Greeks called it *opallios*, a word coined from two other words, the first of which gives us words such as opaque and optical, while the other gives us words like alias and alter. Thus *opal* literally means 'to see a change (of colour).'

Opal is known in Indonesia. The Indonesian name *kalimaya* is derived from the Sanskrit *maya*, an illusion, and the Javanese *kali* which means a river. The result is 'a river of illusion,' which is not altogether unlike seeing a change in colour.

The Aztec term for Mexican opal is *vitzitziltecpatl*, or 'the humming-bird stone,' for its change of colours was likened to the sheen found on that creature's plumage.

Opals were produced in Hungary from the gem-mining village of Opalbanya in the eleventh century. But the Greeks and Romans probably obtained what opal they had from Anatolia in Turkey or (as mentioned by Pliny) from India.

At first opals were considered to be lucky because from within them gleamed the talismanic lights of all other precious gems. Then in 1829 Sir Walter Scott published his novel *Anne of Geierstein*. Scott used an opal to reflect brilliantly the changing fortunes of the heroine. But this was unappreciated by a world of literary flunkeys, who in their own minds conjured up the idea that the opal could have properties of evil influence.

The results were remarkably absurd. Twelve months after the publication of Scott's novel, opal was down to half its former high value, and falling rapidly out of fashion. Such was the beginning of the superstition that opal is unlucky.

No other gemstone variety has had so distinguished a history. Wonderful stories of its propensity to attract misfortune arose. The royal house of Spain laid its misfortunes on a single opal belonging to the king, in a way which somewhat reflects the heroine's progress in Scott's story.

Interest in the gemstone next came to the surface in Australia and in Mexico. A Mexican peasant found opal near Queretaro in 1851, but it was nearly another twenty years before any serious work commenced to develop this find in 1871. And in South Australia, in about 1841, a German prospector, Johan Menge, found opal near Angaston in the Barossa Valley. This opal was subsequently displayed at the Great Exhibition in London during 1851.

No mining seems ever to have been carried out in this area, and there is a gap of twenty-two years before another find is recorded. In 1863, the Reverend John Bleasdale recorded the presence of opals in the Beechworth mining district in northern Victoria. These are reputed to have been waterworn amygdules, which were recovered during gold sluicing, and which showed a fair amount of colour play. In 1870 another report lists the occurrence of fine nodular pieces of opal in basalt near Sunbury and in a vesicular basalt layer near Gelantipy, Gippsland. This opal was abundantly dispersed through the rock in small rounded grains. Another occurrence in the Snowy Mountains is of opal associated with granite. However, despite the tremendous interest of gem and mineral societies in Victoria at the present time, to date not one of these deposits has ever been worked.

In 1872 opal was found at two places in Queensland. One was on Listowel Downs Station in the centre of the colony, and again no work has ever been done to develop this deposit. The other was in the little central town of Springsure. And from Springsure came the first mining and subsequent sale of Australian opal ever recorded. It was discovered by a store employee, a Mr O'Brien, and afterwards held under lease by the local telegraph officer, T. F. Batho.

Batho's mine was in rocks of volcanic origin—basalts, tuffs, and rhyolites—containing small vesicles or gas bubbles in which the opal occurred. The colour play of the opal has been described as ranging from light blue to green, vivid green, and deep green in different specimens. The deep green samples show flashes of a vivid red when viewed from a suitable angle.

But, as is always the case, such opals were the exception rather than the rule and, although four shafts were sunk through the weathered zone of the volcanic rocks, it was soon found that the ground became more dense with depth and too difficult to work without ruining any opal that was discovered.

These opals were only bean-sized when recovered, and so this deposit did not attract as much attention as the other finds that suddenly mushroomed throughout western Queensland during 1873. The news spread fast. Opals had been found along the Bulloo River and were bringing high prices. Men came, urged on by their eager anticipation of the treasures they were going to unearth. But trouble came too, for uprisings occurred among the Aborigines over their mistreatment.

The next man we know to be associated with opal was Herbert Bond, who in 1875 registered a company in Pall Mall, London, to develop some of these Queensland opal deposits. The company was heavily financed, and there were twelve claims in its holdings.

The Grey Range became the scene for a sudden rash of opal-mining fever after 1877, and that country opened up at an exciting pace. The Australian stagecoach line, Cobb & Co., had 6000 horses on the roads in the three eastern colonies, and they penetrated into the western Queensland tracts by swinging their coaches west from Charleville, following the miners and prospectors. They brought with them speculators to view the land, and even more miners to reinforce the band of bush workers. Coaching stages were quickly developed and just as quickly proclaimed town sites, even before names were found for them. Blackwater, Quilpie, and Kyabra were so founded.

Shanties were thrown together. By the middle of 1878 the storekeepers had arrived. Adavale and Eromanga, dusty little townships that they were, became inland centres of the continent, and they were there to stay. The coaches kept sweeping west, carrying the rudiments of civilisation in their wake. The centres of Thargomindah, Eulo, Hungerford, Tinnenburra, and Barringun developed as links on the intricate chain forged by the Cobb & Co. stages as they conquered this loneliness by establishing lines of communication through the wilderness.

The stations, however, became concerned about their loss of labour as the opal fields lured the stockmen away. By the end of 1878 the opalers were out among the stony ridges at Eromanga, and opal fever had spread further west across the channels and out to Windorah near the border. But opal mining proved to be hard, tedious work—digging holes and cracking rocks under the orange heat of the central Australian sun. Water was not plentifully available, ever! And machinery was not to be had to win this gem. The work remained a tough pick-and-shovel game.

About this time, the collapse of Herbert Bond's company spelled the end to the miners' market. But the interest was maintained. Fortune was a goddess promising great and imminent wealth to her devotees. The realm of her domain continued to push forth and opal was discovered at Opalton in 1888, in the Paroo area in 1893, and at Kynuna, the most northern worked occurrence, in 1894.

It is now realised that in western Queensland there are over 400 000 square kilometres of suitable host rocks in which precious opal can occur at any place which conforms with the geological requirements for opal formation. But back in those days, prospectors searched the ground for float—loose pieces of opal weathered out on to the surface—worthless in itself, but exciting for its promise.

It is now time to meet the founder of the Australian opal industry, Tully Cornthwaite Wollaston. In 1888, at the age of twenty-five, he heard about opal mining in Queensland and he became fired with enthusiasm to make his fortune with this gemstone. Finance was his immediate problem, so he organised a syndicate to back him. Then on 21 November 1888 he and a companion set out overland from Adelaide to find a prospector named Joe Bridle in the hot Kyabra Hills, somewhere in central Queensland.

Wollaston's record in his book, *Opal, the Gem of the Never Never*, makes vivid reading. They travelled by train to Marree, where camels were hired, and then overland through the Birdsville Track country. Eventually, on 10 January 1889, they reached Bridle's camp at the Stoney Creek opal mine. They had travelled in the heat of summer, during the worst drought then recorded, and traversed 1100 kilometres of arid countryside in seven weeks.

The enterprise undoubtedly sounded ridiculous, and was criticised as such by his stay-at-home friends. But it succeeded.

At first Wollaston was dismayed at the opal Bridle had to show him. It was pale in colour, spotted with sandy holes, and had bars of ironstone cut through it. There was nothing to encourage him here! Bridle showed him his mine. 'If this is an opal mine, God help the shareholders,' he thought. More disappointment! Moving out on all fours, Wollaston crawled through the low passages. The candle light lit up something which twinkled like the star, Sirius, on a clear night. It was a fragment of true, gem opal. High-class opal was to be found here after all!

Bridle decided to trust Wollaston, and from his cache took out his top-grade stones, sixty-one pieces of small opal gems alive with glowing fire. Wollaston made his first purchase, and with this material was able to make his first sales overseas. Arrangements were made to peg the Stoney Creek, Exhibition, Southern Gem, and Breakfast Creek opal areas, after agreement had been reached with the men working them.

Then, after returning to Adelaide, Wollaston went to Europe. He was full of enthusiasm, but the London wholesale gem merchants were not interested in his stone. The English, used to the pale Hungarian opal, if they had seen opal at all, were not enamoured with the superior Australian variety from Queensland.

Wollaston next approached jewellers, but found that they were suspicious or not interested. At last he found in Hasluck Bros of 104 Hatton Garden a business firm ready to give this new opal a chance. A lapidary was engaged and there the first parcels of cut Australian opals were prepared for the American market.

This sale of opal returned a high profit, but Wollaston found that his investors at home never recognised this. Returning to Australia, he was dismayed to find that cheques drawn on the syndicate were dishonoured. The syndicate was not prepared to explore the leases he had taken out, but was inclined to condemn them, and was more desirous of selling scrip in the business than gaining supplies of any opal that could be bought.

Wrath and impatience drove him out to see the mines again and to deliberate over the whole situation. He withdrew from the syndicate and, with his leaving, the Western Queensland Opal Mining Company Ltd suffered a natural demise.

Back on the Stoney Creek field, he heard news of a new find. This time another old miner, Bill Johnson, showed him the most glorious opals, which he described as 'sacred balls of fire which tumbled into a glowing pool.'

There were sixty pieces of pure red-grained opal as large as walnuts in his firsts, and his seconds and thirds were by no means poor relations.

Wollaston examined this collection with his heart pounding. All the opal he had ever seen paled into insignificance beside the pile of gems from this new mine, the Little Wonder. 'If old Bill had demanded a villa on Lake Como, or the Elgin Marbles and a life pension,' he later recalled, 'or any other trifles like these as a condition of sale, I should have closed with him instantly. But the price was merely "one thousand quid," expressed in a nervous and half defiant tone.' Today we would consider such a sum to be a fraction of the value of any one of those sixty top-grade stones.

The journey back to Adelaide with his booty from the Little Wonder mine was made as rapidly as possible, for it seemed to Wollaston that even the crows could be conspiring to rob him of his prize. And when he finally reached home a fresh surprise awaited him.

Some opal specimens had been sent to him from a place a hundred kilometres north of Wilcannia in New South Wales, by an old workmate, Charlie Turner. These stones were like the white Hungarian type in appearance. They occurred as flat cakes of solid opal and were quite free of adhering matrix. They were sunbleached pieces, but still of some value to collectors, and had weathered out of the hillsides to become strewn on the surface.

After only two days in Adelaide, Tully Wollaston found himself bounding back inland again, to Broken Hill by train, and then by coach to Wilcannia, and then north on a buckboard to a kangaroo shooters' camp—a camp soon to be known around the world as the celebrated White Cliffs opal mines, the most productive opal field yet known in the whole world.

One of the kangaroo shooters, George Hooley, met Wollaston along the track with a horse, and together they rode over to the camp, where some shallow workings had been carried out. An opal seam had been encountered, and some good-quality gemstone had been fossicked out. But the shooters were at a loss to know what value to give it, and so was Wollaston, who admits, 'I did not know much; they knew nothing.' He was new to this new industry, and decided to risk £140, which he considered to be a fair offer. On his naming the figure, there was a great calm. The men were simply paralysed, but only for an instant, and then eight eager hands shot out! Just imagine it! For a week four men had been digging up pretty stones, and now they were offered over a half a year's earnings each for their samples, samples which they were going to toss among the gibber rocks anyway after this fellow had gone away. But Wollaston developed organised opal-mining here and made a fortune.

Outward bound once more for England, with two magnificent parcels of precious opal and freed of encumbering directors, Wollaston was now well on the way to establishing, single handed, the Australian opal industry.

He made steady headway in London. Hasluck's engaged six cutters to work on Wollaston's opal. The cut gemstones then sold as fast as they could get them polished. Those wholesalers who sixteen months previously had advised him not to waste his time were now anxious to secure large parcels of rough opal for themselves. So, gradually, Wollaston took to selling parcels of the rough, and within a few years ended by adopting this method altogether, considering it to be the best and the only method of handling volume stocks successfully.

Opal trading was brisk now, and in Australia keen competition developed in both White Cliffs and Queensland. Other firms appointed their own representatives and field buyers, forming a host of lively rivals. Prices took off and continued to soar upwards both at home and abroad.

Controversy on the field existed, however, regarding the market price of opal. Wollaston's organised tributing system fell under much attack, and by 1901 a Royal Commission advised that this form of management be discontinued. As a result there disappeared the one really steady form of management which did exist, and with it the spine of White Cliffs, for it was not replaced with anything else.

The general opinion was that opal could be found only on the blocks area at White Cliffs, despite the fact that opal had been found and worked as far away as Purnanga, sixty kilometres to the north in 1896, and at The Bunker, nineteen kilometres to the south-west. Both these newer fields produced white opal, similar to that found at White Cliffs. White opal had originally been identified in New South Wales during 1881 from near the Mount Brown goldfield in the far north-western corner of the colony. This deposit has never been touched.

It took another thirteen years, however, before the White Cliffs field became deserted, and this happened abruptly with the outbreak of the first World War and the withdrawal of Germany as a major overseas market.

During this time other finds were recorded. Opal was found by a Mr Morris on his property, at Tintenbar, New South Wales, in 1901, but it took another eighteen years before this was mined, in 1919. It has also been located nearby at Bex Hill and more recently at Mount Bougrom near Mullumbimby, and Nimbin as well. In the Western Australian gold-mining town of Coolgardie, opal with a play of colours was found in 1903, but this did not prove to be of commercial value. Eighty kilometres eastwards at Canowna Downs more opal has been located.

And in South Australia, in 1904, opal was found near a place called Charley's Swamp, between Lake Torrens and Lake Eyre. But the quality did not match that from White Cliffs, as it had gypsum inclusions of 'sandy whisker.' Solely on that account, no further exploration has been encouraged. There remains the possibility that there may be here a vast opal field, imploring someone to try it and to find quality opal.

Quality opal, however, is not always readily recognised, as the discoverer of the Lightning Ridge field found out. Charlie Nettleton, that successful miner, sold his first parcel of black opal from Wallungulla, an area now called Lightning Ridge, for £15 in 1903. Difficulty arose in selling this opal because it was so dark. The first parcel found weighed 2·4 kilograms and was sent to the Sydney jewellers, Richard Nelson. They declared it valueless and returned it, offering a mere ten shillings for the lot. Yet by 1908 black opal was fetching fifty times the value Nettleton obtained.

To try to sell, Nettleton took this new, unsaleable black opal overland to T. C. Wollaston at White Cliffs. Again confronted with something new, Wollaston immediately saw its phenomenal potential and bought, determined to introduce this outstanding gem to a reluctant market.

It took time for the Wallungulla field to develop. At first only thirty men worked there, but by 1906 the field was becoming talked about and was attracting men from the now fading White Cliffs. And no wonder! White Cliffs is hot, barren, and parched. Compared with White Cliffs, this area at Lightning Ridge was a paradise. It has an annual rainfall of fifty centimetres, and grass, trees, and scrub adorn the countryside. In those days game was plentiful—kangaroos, emus, wild turkeys, and rabbits were everywhere.

Lightning Ridge has become famous for its black opal. Frequently, and wrongly, it is described as the only place in the world from which black opal is produced. A little black opal has been found in White Cliffs, and in several places in Queensland, as well as in Tintenbar and Andamooka. Black opal of quality was located at Mintabie in the north of South Australia too, in 1919. In 1906, black opal was found and worked in the Virgin Valley, Nevada, and a magnificent, fiery black precious opal is now being mined in Java, Indonesia.

Lightning Ridge produces a high-grade light opal too, and the intervening years between discovery and acceptance of black opal were only possible at Lightning Ridge because of the ready sale of the light opal.

In 1907 some scrub clearers found opal floaters west of Lightning Ridge, and more workings commenced. A new field developed, the Grawin black opal field. Black opal was also found another eight kilometres away at Glengarry, and another fifty kilometres north of Lightning Ridge at the Billy Goat Hill and Meehi fields, New Angledool. And further north, on into Queensland, opal has been located at Imenbah Station, Narran Station, and Barney's Ridge, near Goodooga.

Other opal traces have been found in New South Wales, at Lila Springs, at Brindingabba, and at Barringun. This was white opal, and has never been worked either. More fields obviously remain to be discovered.

Floaters of light opal were found in South Australia during 1915. J. R. Hutchinson gives a graphic account of this discovery in the *Adelaide Chronicle* of 7 April 1938. Just picture a prospecting party looking for gold in the lonely centre of that State. Soon they were looking for water in order to survive. No gold. No water. At dusk on 6 February 1915 the party returned to camp, still with no water. Jim Hutchinson had left his fifteen-year-old son, Bill, at camp on this particular day. Now that the father had returned, his son was found to be gone. He could perish in the desert if he was lost, and it was very easy to get lost here. There was no possible chance of picking up his tracks until daylight. The men collected what dry mulga wood they could find to make a beacon fire to light his way back to camp. Just as they were about to set it alight, Bill quietly strolled into the camp.

He threw down a sack half full of opal, and said, 'Have a look at that, Dad. I think you'll find some good stuff there.'

He had found water too, and this lasted them for eight days, after which the party was forced to give up looking for opal float and return to Adelaide. Hutchinson sent the opal to T. C. Wollaston, who was now the leading world authority on opals. His judgement on this material was that, being bleached and sun crazed, it was worthless. But it did indicate that opals were present in the region!

Word got around. Two experienced opalers from White Cliffs, the brothers Jim and Dick O'Neill, headed for the field. When they arrived, they did not like the look of the place, so they struck further north again and they found quality opal. They immediately pegged several large blocks, no doubt thinking to recreate in South Australia the tributing system of working that had existed in New South Wales. Wollaston bought their first parcel of gemstones in 1915. The O'Neills found £17,000 pounds worth in their first nine months. This would be over a quarter of a million dollars in value today. The first shipment of this opal, from a place just labelled on the map as Stuart's Range, was taken in 1916 to the United States, where trade, despite the war, was being carried on.

But the South Australian Government did not ratify the extensive leases applied for by these firstcomers, and special claims for opal miners were introduced. So, in 1918, the potential opal field was made available for all newcomers to take as much ground as they could conveniently work.

To encourage opal mining, the South Australian Government constructed water tanks at the field. Eventually a mail service was begun and a commissioner appointed to promote opal trade overseas. Conditions of field life became good enough now for some men to bring their families to live in the area and, as a town developed, so did the extent of the field. Opal has now been found extensively northwards and southwards from the township along the line of the range, and opalisation has been traced for over one hundred kilometres.

During 1925 this settlement was officially given the name of Coober Pedy, supposedly Aboriginal words meaning 'a man in a hole.'

Government assistance and stimulation meant that men were encouraged to find opal. And find it they did. Black opal was found at Mintabie, 320 kilometres north-west of Coober Pedy, by an old Territorian named Larry O'Toole. Here the country is extremely harsh and uninviting. Long, low ridges dwindle away into the infinity of the encompassing desert, which holds the secret of opal.

And the secret is held well, for it is hard rock in which this Mintabie opal is formed, not the soft clays of the other fields. Some holes were sunk, and these required the use of explosives. Some even defied this treatment. Search continued, and by 1931 opal had been found widely in the surrounding ten kilometres, on properties named Sailor's Well, Mount

Johns, Granite Downs, Welbourn Hill, Eavina Hill, Lambina, Mount Brady, Ouldaburra Hill, and Sarda Bluff.

Opals have also been found in South Australia in several other remote places. These include Anna Creek, Innamincka, Lake Hart, Myall Creek, Oodnadatta, Roxby Downs, The Twins, and Yarrawurta Cliff, but no workings have been developed at these places.

The next important discovery in the grand story of Australia's opal-mining history was a chance find on another property, Andamooka Station. Andamooka is 600 kilometres north of Adelaide. The undulating countryside is dry and covered with gibbers. Most of the scant vegetation is carried by low sandhills which relieve the monotony of the arid landscape. As one approaches Andamooka, the land becomes noticeably more hilly and the sand-dunes become more prominent.

R. W. Segnit tells the story in the *South Australian Mineral Review* No. 62 (1935) pp 51–56. He says that opal was first discovered accidentally by two boundary riders, Sam Brooks and Ray Shepherd, on the side of what is now known as Treloars Hill. The opal was identified by Bruce McK. Foulis, the manager of Andamooka Station, on 29 August 1930, and was first worked by two employees, Alan Treloar and Paddy Evans. Q. Le M. Knight, writing in *The Australian Museum Magazine* of December 1961, tells of the efforts made to keep the discovery a secret. Bruce Foulis smuggled in four diggers from Port Augusta and they, with Alan Treloar and another station hand, Jack Hughes, worked the claim in 1931. Although the secret had been closely guarded, in due course the news did leak out and there was a rush of newcomers from Coober Pedy, 240 kilometres to the north-west.

Andamooka was officially declared an opal field in 1933, but despite the rushes, the numbers that went to White Cliffs were never seen here, although Andamooka opal is a top-quality gemstone. Probably the main reason for this apparent disinterest was that prices were low during the Depression, and the lure of possible instantaneous wealth seemed more remote to the general public than ever before. Economic fluctuations apart, opal mining at Andamooka has developed a tremendous stability. Many consider it the premier opal-producing field of the world today, particularly since other occurrences of the precious stone have been found to the south at White Dam and Edge Hill Dam, and north-eastwards at Yarrawurta Cliff.

Opal had already been found northwards from Andamooka as long ago as 1904, at Charlie's Swamp. In 1947 another find was made sixteen kilometres away from that at Stuart's Creek. But no work of sufficient nature to test these opal occurrences was ever done.

Probably the main reason for this lack of follow-up was the discovery of fabulous opal at Coober Pedy in 1946. An Aboriginal woman found opal at shallow depth on the upper Coober Pedy plateau, thirteen kilometres west of the town. This gave a rebirth to the local industry, and twenty years later, the bulk of gemstone from Coober Pedy was being won from workings in this area.

Essentially, however, the conditions of the Australian opal-mining scene remained static. In 1956, only about thirty men were engaged in gouging at Coober Pedy, about the same number at Andamooka, and probably only ten at Lightning Ridge. Opal mining in Queensland was at a complete standstill. Then mechanisation came.

At Andamooka, Frank Schulten installed the first power-operated equipment in 1956. It was a pneumatic spade. Schulten claimed that this equipment enabled him to prospect in a month as much ground as he formerly explored in a year. By 1959, bulldozing was another means of opal mining introduced at Andamooka in the Horse Paddock area. By 1963, truck-mounted Calweld drilling-rigs were sinking one-metre-diameter shafts into the opal stratum. The rigs have since been introduced with much enthusiasm into all the workings in Australia.

Other forms of mining improvements have been seen too. At Lightning Ridge motor-driven puddling machines boosted opal production temporarily while they were put to use sieving through most of the old tailings on the field, recovering material either missed or discarded in past years. From this the wet puddler evolved, and most, if not all, of the opal stratum mined from Lightning Ridge is treated by that means today.

In Queensland, open cutting with bulldozers to reveal the large ironstone boulder concretions is the usual manner of looking for opal.

During the early 1970s, some opal-mining companies set out to find economic quantities of opal, but failed because they were still using the same hit-and-miss methods that had been used in the years gone by. Opal can be found by scientific, geological means, and this little known aspect is discussed in chapter six.

The value of opal is something else which is little realised in Australia. Opal Mining Consultants of Sydney has calculated that if all the opal in Australia could be mined and sold, and the price sustained at the levels current today, it would be worth $50 million million!

That black opal is worth a lot of money is generally well known, but a remarkable ignorance on the subject exists even right through the trade. This trade has not equipped itself with a reliable categorisation of opal types or patterns. And there has not been a logical way of estimating the value of opal, or a way of explaining to an unaware populace what a remarkable substance opal is. This guide will assist everyone with these points which we lack.

QUALIFYING OPAL

Opal is a true precious stone which occurs in many varied forms. Let us first consider what it is. Opal is amorphous silica with a water content varying from one to twenty percent, depending on the porosity and degree of hydration. Precious opal usually contains from six to ten percent water.

Opal may be dull and valueless, in which case it is called *common opal*; only vividly coloured opal qualifies as *precious opal*. Common opal occurs in abundance throughout the world. One form found in association with opal of value, is *potch*. Potch is an interesting word, and probably is a miners' corruption of *potsherd*, or *pot-shard*, meaning a broken piece. Such material originally was called *schnide* on the White Cliffs field in the very early days. Since one variety, crockery potch, has the appearance of broken pottery, it is quite feasible that 'potsherd' has been the basis of this new noun.

In colour, potch may be white, grey, black, amber; it may be honey-coloured, watery clear, or a mixture of these colours. Transparent amber potch is *girasol*, or fire opal. When exceptionally transparent and bright yellow, this fire opal is called sun opal. Another potch variety is called after the magpie on account of the tonal intermixing of black and white. Good quality potch, especially the black variety, is used for the backing in opal doublet manufacture. White potch from Coober Pedy is also used for this purpose. Hyalite is a glassy, clear potch and *hydrophane* is a potch which, only when wetted, shows a definite but weak play of colours.

Another form of opal is composed of alternating potch bands with bars of opal showing a colour play. This is known as *potch with bars.*

About ninety-five percent of opal from the opal fields is potch. Only five percent is of any value. Of this five percent about ninety-five percent is of mediocre grade, with only five percent of real value. It is this small percentage—five percent of five percent—that constitutes the magnificent opal which we call *precious opal*. Any other opal showing a play of colour, but which is not equal in grade to the tops, is *noble opal*, as is girasol and hydrophane.

Australian fire opals: sun opal, Minyon Falls, N.S.W., and Aranjado opal, Andamooka, S.A.

Opal is a precious stone.

Top grade solid opal is *precious opal*.

Other brightly coloured opal is *noble opal*.

It must be understood that this precious-opal classification refers only to rough opal from which solid stones can be cut, *or* to finished gems which are solid stones. Top-grade doublets or triplets are classified as noble opal, not precious, because their opal content is a veneer.

Queensland boulder opal, of top quality and thick enough to have a polished cabochon dome, is still called precious opal, despite the fact that it is not 100 percent opal, but rather opal on ironstone; otherwise it is logically enough classified as noble opal.

Solid opal is opal which is of natural occurrence and solid enough to be set as a gem. Any pieces which need reinforcing (as happens in a doublet) are not solid opal, nor are any pieces which have a non-opal backing, such as Mexican black basaltic opal matrix or boulder opal with a backing of ironstone.

There are other forms which we cannot classify as solid. These include any materials which show small detracting patches in the face of the cut specimen and which are either non-opal or opal lacking colour play. Andamooka opal matrix and Queensland opal-in-matrix are two types which, even if extremely attractive, are not solid opal. Still, they can be classified as *solid matrix*.

Contra Luz is another opal variety found in Mexico and in the volcanic opal areas along Australia's eastern coast. It reveals a colour play by transmitted light.

The term *true opal* is used to describe a fine play of colour which can be seen in the cut stone, no matter from what angle the face is being examined. It is a valuable property. The harlequin opal pattern, on account of its many spangles of colour play, always gives a fine show of brilliant colours from all angles, and this quality of being *true* is an important feature of its value. Indeed the harlequin pattern is considered to be the most valuable of all opal patterns.

TYPES OF OPAL

There are several types of opal. They include:
Andamooka Opal Matrix
Aranjado
Black Opal
Black Crystal Opal
Blue Opal
Boulder Opal
Cherry Opal
Claro-O-Translucente
Contra Luz Opal
Crystal Opal
Fire Opal
Girasol
Golden Opal
Grey Opal
Hydrophane
Hydrophobe
Jelly Opal
Light Opal
Liquid Opal
Mexican Black Basaltic
    Opal Matrix
Mexican Blue Opal
Opal Pseudomorphs
Queensland Opal-in-Matrix

Sedimentary Opal
Semi Black Opal
Sun Opal
Synthetic Opal
Tea Opal
Volcanic Opal
Water Opal
White Opal

HARLEQUIN PATTERN OPAL

Any discussion on opal patterns should commence with *harlequin*, the most prized of all patterns in this fiery gem. Some people think that the term 'harlequin' is applied exclusively to a colour play which manifests itself in the form of chequerboard squares, as the dogma of Australian opal-mining history would have it. Such a pattern can occur, and when it does it is a very rare and exceedingly valuable design for the gemstone. However, other patterns also qualify as 'harlequin.' Harlequin opal is precious opal in which the colours shine as patches or spangles. The patches are regular with definite boundaries, and are distributed in a way that forms a mosaic composition, the appearance of which is truly magnificent. The term originates from the spangled costume worn by harlequin clowns.

This description was in force to describe opal from the Hungarian mines before any Australian opal had ever been heard of. Why then has a misleading description gained such prominence in Australia and consequently around the world, to the detriment of all the true harlequin-pattern opal that Australia does produce? Undoubtedly it was due to a hoax played by unscrupulous buyers in the early days of the opal industry in Australia. Knowledgable buyers would have known what harlequin opal pattern was and what type of opal it applied to. By rigidly restricting the term to describe only those rare opals actually carrying a chequer-board pattern of squares, these wily fellows duped the miners and were able to buy much true harlequin opal cheaply and later sell it in Europe at premium prices.

Let me now give my definition of harlequin opal.

True precious opal showing a regular mosaic-like chromatic pattern in rounded, angular, or roughly square patches of about equal size, presenting a spangled appearance, is harlequin opal.

With this point established, we can look further and classify many of the descriptive terms applied to precious opal and see that they are subgroups of a harlequin pattern. These, in alphabetical order, are:

ASTERIA HARLEQUIN

A rare formation showing elongated colour units radiating outwards from a central nucleus.

Asteria harlequin pattern. The units of colour play radiate outwards from a nucleus, giving a likeness to a star

Asteria harlequin pattern

BLUE HARLEQUIN

Gems exhibiting all other properties of the definition, but which have a pronounced colour play in the one hue.

Blue harlequin pattern

Blue harlequin chaff pattern in black opal

CHEQUERBOARD HARLEQUIN

Regularly arranged, square-shaped units of the colour design. This is very rare.

Doublet revealing a high degree of uniformity in squares with a magnificent harlequin chequers or chequerboard pattern (C. Totterdell collection, Parramatta, N.S.W.)

Chequerboard harlequin pattern in an Andamooka triplet

Chequerboard harlequin pattern in an Andamooka triplet

Chequerboard harlequin pattern (C. Totterdell collection, Parramatta, N.S.W.)

27

CLOVERLEAF HARLEQUIN

Units of colour forming a cloverleaf design, by having a central unit surrounded by a ring of outer units.

Green cloverleaf harlequin pattern

Cloverleaf harlequin pattern in a superb pair of matching Lightning Ridge black opal doublets, set with white diamonds in pendoloque earrings—personal collection of Mrs E. G. Sherman; photograph courtesy E. Gregory Sherman Pty Ltd

FISHSCALE HARLEQUIN

A pattern resembling a fishscale design, but the terminology in a fashion-conscious market is deplorable today. I consider it better to classify it as a Flag Harlequin.

Fishscale harlequin pattern

Fishscale harlequin pattern black opal

FLAG HARLEQUIN

A colour pattern resembling a three-cornered flagstone paving.

The ultimate in perfection of a harlequin pattern. Regular polyhedra of multi-coloured opal, neatly arranged in a flag harlequin display (E. Gregory Sherman collection, Sydney)

Triplet showing flag harlequin pattern in brilliant colours (E. Gregory Sherman Collection, Sydney)

Flag harlequin black opal, Lightning Ridge

Large cabochon of Coober Pedy white opal exhibiting flag harlequin pattern. Each segment of irisations is distinctly and abruptly edged. Scale: crosses 1 cm apart vertically (E. Gregory Sherman collection, Sydney)

FLAGSTONE HARLEQUIN

A pattern resembling the design of an irregular flagstone path.

Fiery flagstone harlequin semiblack opal, Coober Pedy. Note the red emerging out of the blue (Author's collection, Sydney)

A free-form flagstone harlequin white opal, Coober Pedy (Opal Spectrum collection, Coober Pedy)

FLORAL HARLEQUIN

A splashy effect of units which can be likened to the bright floral patterns of dress materials, or to bunches of flowers. Three or more units of colour, closely grouped together, make up a flower. This, too, is a very rare pattern.

Floral harlequin pattern in black opal, Lightning Ridge. The striking complementaries, red and green, are arranged in an unmistakable red flower and green foliage display

A fiery floral harlequin doublet, showing red rising out of the blue, the most valuable of all opal colours (E. Gregory Sherman collection, Sydney)

The ultimate in perfection, floral harlequin light opal from Andamooka. Scale: crosses 1 cm apart vertically (E. Gregory Sherman collection, Sydney)

An incredibly refulgent mass of colour irisations arranged in a floral harlequin pattern, Coober Pedy (E. Gregory Sherman collection, Sydney)

Floral harlequin pattern boulder opal,
Queensland

Grey opal showing a floral harlequin pattern

GREEN HARLEQUIN

Gems exhibiting all other properties of the definition, but which have a pronounced green hue.

Green harlequin pattern seen in dyed Andamooka opal matrix

Green harlequin pattern shown off by a triplet

HEXAGONAL HARLEQUIN

A very rare pattern showing hexagonal colour units arranged together in an interlocking design.

This extremely rare pattern in Lightning Ridge black opal shows hexagons arranged together in an interlocking design, representing an extraordinary degree of continuous hexagonal stacking of the basic building particles into a pseudo-crystalline structure exhibiting triadic colour harmony in red, blue, and green. (Photograph: courtesy of Dr Archie Kalokerinos)

PALETTE HARLEQUIN

A pattern with widely spaced units, similar to the layout of colours on an artist's palette.

Palette harlequin black opal

Palette harlequin pattern

SQUARE HARLEQUIN

Squarish disjointed colour units are present in the opal pattern.

Harlequin squares is the basic pattern of this triplet of Brazilian opal

There are a few other sub-varieties of the harlequin pattern which occur occasionally. However, there is no point in pedantically trying to classify all harlequin patterns into these varieties, for they represent an uncommon and unusual perfection of form. But when the design unmistakably belongs to one of these categories, then it should be nominated as such. This is important for Australia's opal industry, as an accepted standardisation should be universally used, for opals represent an outstanding form of investment. The Australian opal industry will be taking a step forward to protect itself and to promote the image of opals by using commonsense descriptions of its products.

Not all opal has a harlequin pattern, and we must examine the various other forms of design and categorise them, too. We need a simple description of precious opal patterns. Opal is full of change; it quivers in the light and transmutes from red to green, to blue and back to orange. It flashes and rolls. We are not faced with a mere academic job to describe any pattern, but rather a very practical one. Any collector or dealer can clearly gain a concise understanding of any gem when it is properly described.

It is well to remember, however, that the occurrence of any pattern, whether harlequin or other, is not common, and one piece of opal may exhibit several forms of pattern. With opal patterns the rule is the exception, but a true patterned gem possesses a factor which increases its rarity and so its value.

These are the patterns, set out in alphabetical order:

Abanderada	Lechosos
Azules	Liquid
Blue	Lluvisnando
Broken Flash	Mackerel Sky
Chaff	Moss
Chinese Writing	Night Stone
Contra Luz	Pinfire
Exploding Flash	Peacock's Tail Pinfire
Eye-of Opal	Rainbow
Fiery	Ribbon
Flame	Rolling Flash
Flash of Fire	Scotch Plaid
Flash	Star
Golden	Starflash
Gossamer Veil	Straw
Grass	Sunflash
Green	Tree or Fern Pinfire
Iris	Twinkle

ABANDERADA

A Mexican term describing the pattern formed from the sedimentary or banded build-up of colour horizons, which gives a banded or flag-stripe effect. This pattern notably occurs in Queensland boulder opal.

Abanderada pattern in boulder opal, Bulls Creek, Queensland

Abanderada harlequin pattern in Queensland boulder opal (L. Withers collection, Sydney)

AZULES

A jelly-type opal with a haze of blue-mauve irisations.

Azules-type opal, Coober Pedy

Azules-type opal exhibiting the reflected orange glow typical of scattered light after passing through a colloidal suspension

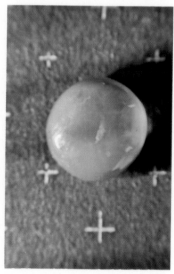

BLUE

A variety of opal in which brilliant blue, indigo, and violet are prominent. It can be used in combination with other terms, e.g. *blue flash black opal*, or *blue harlequin black opal*.

Blue pinfire black opal

Blue broken flash black opal

BROKEN FLASH

Similar to Flash pattern, but there are two or more areas of colour present. These extinguish in turn as the stone is rotated, so that only part of the stone is displaying colour at any one time.

Triplet exhibiting a harlequin arrangement of broken flash pattern. Scale: crosses 1 cm apart (E. Gregory Sherman collection, Sydney)

Broken flash pattern

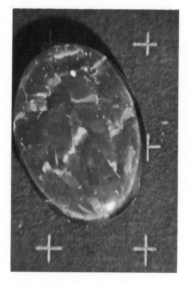

CHAFF

Intermixed and indefinitely rounded colour units, exhibiting very distinguishable packing-fault lineations in each unit. Such lineations are all aligned in each unit and are randomly distributed in natural opal.

Chaff pattern harlequin opal. Each segment of colour in the stone is striated by multiple, parallel, stacking-fault lineations, which give the pattern the appearance of chopped chaff

Chaff pattern in black opal

CHINESE WRITING
A fanciful description of either potch or opal slashed with a differently patterned noble opal. There is a similarity to Chinese calligraphy.

Chinese writing pattern in ring-set black opal, Lightning Ridge, N.S.W.

CONTRA LUZ

Opal showing colour play when viewed against the light.

Contra luz volcanic opal liquid pattern, Tintenbar, N.S.W.

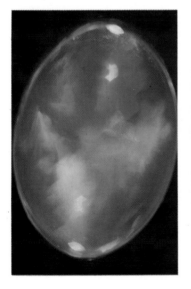

Contra luz colour play in volcanic opal from Tintenbar, N.S.W. (Author's collection, Sydney)

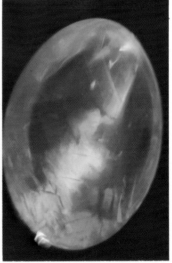

EXPLODING FLASH

A flash pattern which appears to explode outwards in all directions as the stone is moved.

Left and right: Triplet illustrating the flash pattern's extremes—from complete annihilation of colour to an intense complete flash of brilliant hues. Scale: name patch = 1 cm (C. Totterdell collection, Parramatta, N.S.W.)

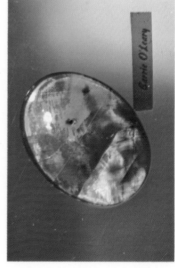

Right, below left and below right: An exploding flash pattern in which the colour changes as the stone is rotated

EYE-OF-OPAL

An eye-like effect created when opal infills a cavity. The Flame Queen is the best-known gem of this type.

A remarkable specimen showing how an original bubble in precious opal exhibiting a green iris pattern has been succeedingly infilled by a rim of opal showing sunflash fire play, and finally the entire resultant cavity has been completely infilled with fiery harlequin-pattern opal

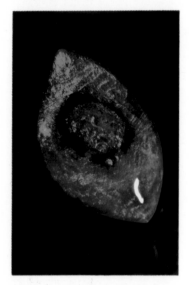

FIERY

A term used to describe any opal which has a dominant red hue in the colour play. Sometimes the term 'red opal' is used.

A fiery pinfire pattern (C. Totterdell collection, Parramatta, N.S.W.)

Fiery starflash pattern in black opal

FLAME

Colours are arranged in a more-or-less regularly streaked effect (rather than in stripes as in *Abanderada*). *Flash-of-fire* is another term to describe the same effect. The stone may need to be turned to a certain angle before the colours resemble the dancing flames from a log fire.

Green flame pattern

Flame pattern in black opal

Blue flame pattern

Flame pattern in black opal

FLASH OF FIRE

Another term with *Flame* to describe the effect where the colours resemble the dancing flames from a log fire.

Flash of fire pattern in a magnificent doublet
(E. Gregory Sherman Collection, Sydney)

The same stone, advanced

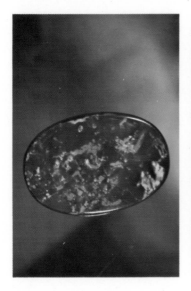

Flash of fire pattern in a triplet. Note the unusual American beauty crimsons exhibited in the colour play of this stone (E. Gregory Sherman collection, Sydney)

The same stone, advanced

FLASH

A striking pattern showing a single pronounced flash of colour right across the whole surface of the cut stone. This chromatic glow will change colour as the piece is turned, and at critical angles it will extinguish and leave the stone looking like blank potch. This is a serious defect, for the piece lacks *trueness*, and this lowers the value.

Flash pattern in superb crystal opal from Duck Creek, Queensland (E. Gregory Sherman Collection, Sydney)

The same stone, advanced

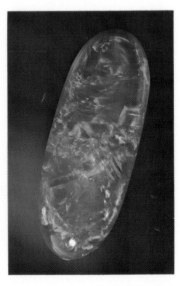

Collection of black opals exhibiting flash pattern, from Tintenbar, N.S.W. (Superior Opal Traders collection, Sydney)

Green flash crystal opal

GOLDEN

Opal showing a predominantly orange-to-yellow colour play, or opal with a golden base tone. It may be combined with other terms, e.g., *golden harlequin opal*.

Golden opal from Queensland. The base has been stained a rich golden colour by iron oxides, undoubtedly associated with the ironstone concretions of the Queensland opal fields. The pattern is a floral harlequin (F. Tyne collection, Kurrajong, N.S.W.)

Golden crystal opal with flash of fire pattern from Duck Creek, Queensland. Scale: Crosses 1 cm apart (E. Gregory Sherman collection, Sydney)

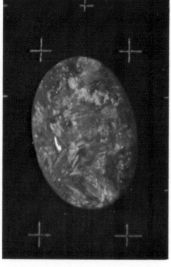

GOSSAMER VEIL

When the colour play of opal is not made up of sharp and distinctive colour units, but rather appears as a floating flimsy gauze of delicate irisations, then the descriptive name for this pattern is 'gossamer veil,' or more simply 'gossamer.' It is not of high monetary worth because of its more plentiful supply and because it lacks the aesthetic appeal and spectral brilliance of harlequin and flash types.

Water opal exhibiting gossamer pattern

Semi black opal from Lightning Ridge, N.S.W., showing liquid irisations arranged in a gossamer pattern (E. Gregory Sherman collection, Sydney)

GRASS

Here the colour units are thinner than in the straw pattern, but still show a packing-fault lineation along their length. The effect can be likened to the appearance of blades of grass.

Grass pattern reminiscent of the appearance of blades of green grass, displayed by a triplet. Scale: name patch = 1 cm (C. Totterdell collection, Parramatta N.S.W.)

GREEN

Any opal showing a predominantly green colour play.

Left and right: Two views of The Moonbeam, showing brilliant green flash in crystal opal, Lightning Ridge (E. Gregory Sherman collection, Sydney)

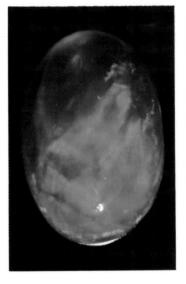 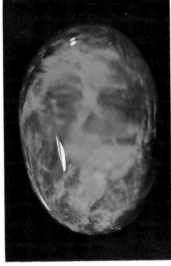

HARLEQUIN

This form has already been discussed, but for completeness the major subdivisions are listed here:

Asteria	Fishscale	Green
Blue	Flag	Hexagonal
Chequerboard	Flagstone	Palette
Cloverleaf	Floral	Square

IRIS PATTERN

Irisation which appears as a colour sheen in opal.

Triplets exhibiting iris pattern with cirrus effect. (C. Totterdell collection, Parramatta, N.S.W.)

Iris-patterned triplets exhibiting a brilliant emerald-green sheen. Scale: name patch = 1 cm

LECHOSOS

A Mexican term which describes a milky-white opal exhibiting green irisations.

Lechosos opal, Coober Pedy

Lechosos-type colourings in moss-patterned white opal from Coober Pedy, S.A. (Author's collection)

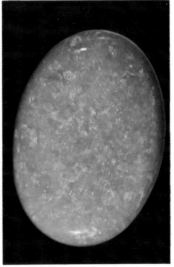

LIQUID

A rare pattern of remarkable mobility which, irrespective of the way the stone is turned, always seems to move in the same direction. It is a feature most often found in volcanic opal. The term should not be confused with a liquid opal gel, as is found at Tintenbar, New South Wales.

A brilliant white lechosos opal showing liquid blue-green irisations, Coober Pedy. Scale: name patch = 1 cm (C. Totterdell collection, Parramatta, N.S.W.)

Contra luz volcanic opal exhibiting liquid pattern Tintenbar, N.S.W.

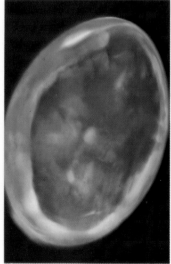

LLUVISNANDO

A Mexican term for a pattern which shows 'sunlight filtering through the waters.'

Black synthetic opal exhibiting lluvisnando pattern (Photograph: Gilson, Switzerland)

MACKEREL SKY

All the spectral colours may be present in this form, which can be likened to a sunset, with clouds broken into long, thin, parallel masses.

Triplet exhibiting mackerel sky pattern (E. Gregory Sherman collection, Sydney)

Triplet exhibiting mackerel sky pattern in reds arising out of blues

MOSS

A dissipated green sheen which resembles the effect of moss.

Green moss pinfire pattern exhibited in a doublet. Scale: name patch = 1 cm (C. Totterdell collection, Parramatta, N.S.W.)

Moss pinfire pattern in light opal

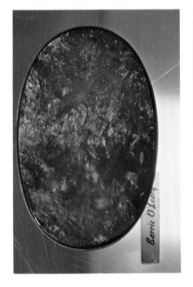

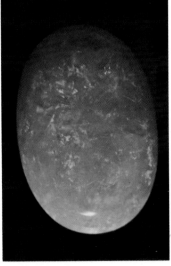

NIGHT STONE

Any opal of such high quality that it has brilliant colour even in dim light, and especially under artificial illumination.

PINFIRE

A pattern characterised by very small or pinpoint-sized specks of colour, less than one millimetre in diameter. This type can be subdivided into *moss*, *peacock's tail*, *tree*, or *fern pinfire*. The most outstanding pinfire is that which presents the colour units in such a way that they radiate as a sheen of the one colour, which changes completely as the stone is viewed from various angles.

Left and right: Magnificent black opal with bright pinfire pattern of colour points, alternating between green and red, depending on the angle viewed, Lightning Ridge. Scale: crosses 1 cm apart (E. Gregory Sherman collection, Sydney)

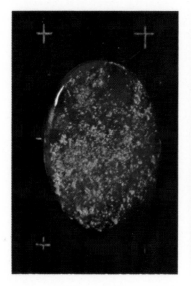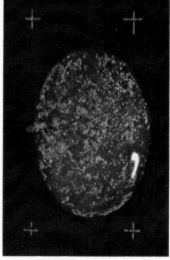

PEACOCK'S TAIL PINFIRE
A distorted pinfire effect in which a bushy or peacock's tail design can be seen.

Peacock's tail pattern, solid white opal, Coober Pedy, S.A. The distinctive effect of radiating pinfire from a central nucleus is like the spread of a peacock's plumage

RAINBOW

Pastel irisation tints closely arranged in successive narrow bands which curve like a rainbow and which merge into each other across the opal. It is noticeably different from the *Abanderada* or *Ribbon* categories.

Rainbow pattern (Superior Opal Traders, Fairfield)

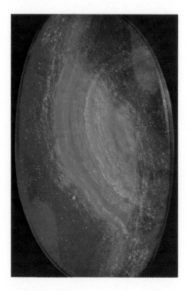

RIBBON

Narrow, parallel stripes of alternating colours, resembling ribbons laid out alongside one another. It is similar to *Abanderada*, but *Abanderada* is wide and fluttering, while *Ribbon* is straight and thin.

Triplet displaying green ribbon pattern (E. Gregory Sherman collection, Sydney)

ROLLING FLASH

A colour flash which rolls from one side of the stone to the other, as the gem is turned. Where there is more than one flash, a *Mackerel Sky* pattern may exist.

Top, left, and right: Rolling flash in black opal, Lightning Ridge

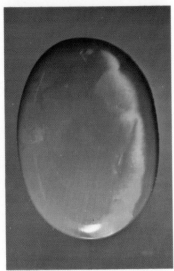

Top, left, and right: Rolling flash pattern

SCOTCH PLAID

This refers to a green-blue effect in black opal, and describes exceptionally wonderful and brilliant colour combinations.

Scotch plaid colours with red rolling flash in black opal, Lightning Ridge. Scale: crosses 1 cm apart (E. Gregory Sherman collection, Sydney)

Scotch plaid flash of fire pattern

STAR

Opal showing a true asterism has been found at Spencer, in Idaho, U.S.A. Dr J. V. Sanders, the discoverer of the reasons for the colour play in opal, has found that these star opals have a face-centred cubic stacking structure parallel to their base, with stacking-faults and twin structure on the three (111) planes. The star in the finished stone is an optical consequence of diffraction from points orientated along these fault planes.

Idaho star opal. Microfaulting along the three (lll) planes of the silica micelles results in light diffraction occurring in three directions which intersect to form a six-rayed star. Diffraction is prominent at one end of each direction in this photograph, forming what appears to be a three-pointed star, but three other rays formed of weaker-appearing diffracted light create a six-rayed asterism effect under direct lighting

Solid black star opal, Glengarry, N.S.W. This is the only known star opal in existence from Australia. Two others were described by T. C. Wollaston in his *Spirit of the Child* in 1914. The true asterism by diffraction oriented along slippage planes in the (111) directions of the basic tetrahedral units gives the distinctive pattern. This collectors' item weighs nearly three carats and has been named by the author the *Marjorie Hope Star Opal* after his mother.

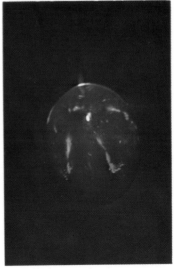

STARFLASH

A form of black potch and colour, in which small points of colour form a speckled star pattern.

Starflash pattern in a doublet (C. Totterdell collection, Parramatta, N.S.W.)

Mixed starflash and moss patterns in Andamooka jelly opal

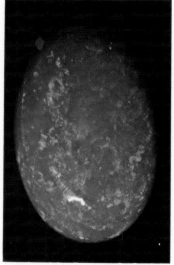

STRAW

A pattern reminiscent of flat straws irregularly overlapping one another.

Straw pattern

SUNFLASH

The colours are very weak and not readily visible unless examined in a strong light source, such as the full sun. It is noble opal and cannot be classified as a gem, but is, rather, a collector's curiosity. Dark pieces of potch show this effect to best advantage because the little colour that is present is best seen against a dark background.

Sunflash opal displaying twinkle pattern

Weak irisations of sunflash-type opal, Lightning Ridge

TREE OR FERN PINFIRE

Elongated pinhead-sized colour units, especially green, which give an impression of foliage, whether it be trees or ferns.

Green fern pinfire pattern in black opal from Tintenbar, N.S.W.

Fern pattern pinfire

TWINKLE

Pinfire variety of pattern in which the point-sized colour units are separated to give a stars-in-the-night effect. The colour is of high intensity. (This term, while most obviously applicable to black opal, can be used to describe any other type as well.)

Red coming out of the blue in twinkle pattern dyed Andamooka opal matrix (Author's collection)

Water opal showing twinkle pattern

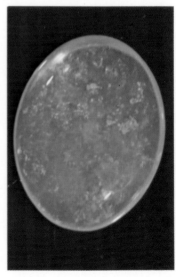

Opals can be properly classified, and this is especially desirable for museums and the trade. To be properly classified, an opal should be fully described according to these points:
(1) its origin, e.g., volcanic or sedimentary
(2) its pattern, which can be additive, e.g., *Scotch plaid harlequin squares*
(3) its type, e.g., black, white, etc.
(4) the location of find.
    Hence, full description could read: *Volcanic flag-harlequin black opal, Tintenbar, N.S.W.*

Green opal twinkle pattern

WHY OPALS HAVE SUCH COLOURS

The reason for the changing play of colours to be seen in noble and precious opal has been the subject of much conjecture. As long ago as 1845 Sir David Brewster, the Scottish physicist, said of opal: 'This gem is intersected in all directions with colorific planes, exhibiting the most brilliant colours of all kinds. The cause of these colours has never, we believe, been carefully studied. Mineralogists have said that they are the colours of thin plates of air occupying fissures or cracks in the stone, but this is a mere assumption, disproved by the fact that no such fissures have ever been found during the processes of cutting out, grinding, and polishing, which the opal undergoes in the hand of the lapidary. In submitting to a powerful microscope specimens of precious opal, and comparing the phenomena with those of hydrophanous opal, it is found that the colorific planes or patches consist of minute pores or vacuities arranged in parallel lines, and that various such planes are placed close to each other, so as to occupy a space with three dimensions.'

In 1862, another scientist, the Frenchman Descloiseaux, described opal in a similar way: 'Some varieties show an internal iridescent colour play of great beauty, which appears bound by the existence of very small interior cavities arranged in parallel rows in regular arrays, which give outstanding flamboyant reflections in good light.'

In 1871, a Professor Behrens made a deep enquiry into the nature of the colour play of opal and concluded that irisation in opal was due to thin curved lamellae, which had originally been formed as parallel plates, but were bent into curves, cracked, and broken up during the time of consolidation of the opal mass. Such lamellae, it was thought, must produce polarisation of light, and their very thinness must have originated colour. For the next ninety-five years, Behrens' ideas dominated gemmological thought on the nature of colour in precious opal.

However, the real breakthrough in understanding the origin of the colour play in opal came when an Australian scientist, Dr J. Sanders, made scanning electron photo-micrographs of different opal varieties in 1964. He found that the difference between common opal and precious opal is in the basic structure of the opal material, and that a complete break in structural properties between opal forms exists. Opal is composed of minute particles of silica in closely packed spherical aggregates of uniform size which have a diameter ranging from 1500 Angstroms to 3500 Angstroms in discrete areas.

Subsequent work revealed that, in gem-quality opal, these silica microspheres are not only remarkably uniform in size, but also they have been able to pack together in a very regular array. As they are spherical in shape there are tiny interstices or 'holes' remaining in the structure between them, and so these holes, too, are arranged in a regular, three-dimensional array. Brewster's hypothesis of 1845 is now proved.

The presence of such an orderly array of minute cavities suggests that opal is an optical diffraction grating for visible light. The separations

Scanning electron photo-micrograph of etched surface of Coolgardie noble opal. The regular periodic array of silica micelles, 3500 Angstrom units in diameter, is clearly portrayed. (Photograph: R. Ball, University of New South Wales)

between the cavities are of just the right dimensions to cause light to be diffracted and, being arranged in a three dimensional array, they cause various wavelengths in the diffracted light to reinforce one another at various angles. So, incident white light is split into its full range of spectral colours—red, orange, yellow, green, blue, indigo, and violet—and thus the colour play in precious opal is seen.

While this theory answers the question as to why colours are seen, it raises the further problem as to how the silica spheres grow and pack together into such incredibly regular arrangements.

Laboratory research in 1966 found that when silica exsolves as free particles from solution, a basic particle becomes a larger one by spontaneous aggregation with other units which position themselves around it. Up to three such shells of spheres are to be found in precious opal. The array composed of the largest size, of 3500 Angstroms diameter,

An opal cameo of Andamooka jelly opal viewed by transmitted light. No colour play is evident and the inherent colour is due to colloidal scattering. Scale: signature patch = 1 cm (C. Totterdell collection, Parramatta, N.S.W.)

Grey vein opal showing distinctive golden potch bars and a gem bar of fiery, flame opal, the whole being offset by a minor, re-cemented fault traversing from the top side to the lower side of the specimen, Grawin, N.S.W. (The Mining Museum of N.S.W., Sydney)

diffracts all colours, but especially red. The array of smallest or one-shell spheres diffract only the blue end of the spectrum. Potch is composed of silica spheres which lack the regular arrangement and are literally dumped together, as well as being distorted and unequal in size.

Some opal is transparent, and even though it possesses a regular array, it still does not show any irisation. This is because a silica cement, which binds the spheres in all opal, has become so continuous that it has completely filled the voids of the structure and so removed or annihilated any light-diffracting arrangement of voids. This form of opal is potch. A similar process of overcementation occurs in various other types of opal, too; for instance, in jelly opal. Here the high lucidity of the stone and the attractive but notably less brilliant colour-effect is due to the voids still being present, but reduced in size and diffracting power.

Further research, in the United States of America, into the nature of opal has found that there are four distinctively different packing modifications in opal apart from potch. These modifications are the result of the rows of spherical silica particles being deposited offset in relation to the lower layer in a rapid succession. This is most evident in precious opal which has parallel bands or striations of a single colour. These bands are

Cabochons of this opal are remarkable for their brilliancy and perfection. These black specimens show a bright flag harlequin pattern of liquid colours. Scale: signature patch = 1 cm (Pierre Gilson, Switzerland)

noticeable because they diffract a different colour from that of the basic area. Electron optical studies confirm that different packing arrangements exist between the unit and the striations. Face-centred cubic-packing structures are alternated with hexagonal closest-packing arrangements as generations of varying slilica deposition.

Other research has made it possible to create synthetic opal in the laboratory. This is done by using silica dissolved in a liquid and, under controlled conditions, letting it settle and form into its basic building blocks, which then stack up into the opal mass. In the process, delicate structures are formed after the fashion of crystals. These are blade-like in appearance and can grow to a length of two centimetres.

Further research has found that heavy faulting exists in the very best opals. This faulting in no way refers to visible cracks and flaws within an

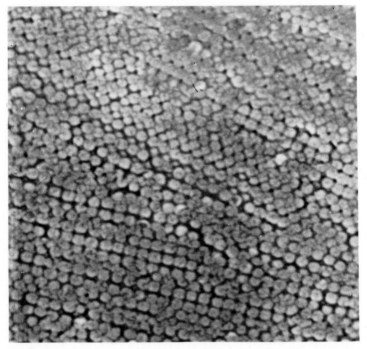

Scanning electron photo-micrograph of fracture surface on Coolgardie noble opal. A grain boundary between two sets of arrays is very noticeable. (Photograph: R. Ball, University of New South Wales)

opal which reduce its value. By 'faulting' we mean the imperfections in the array of silica microspheres. Dr Sanders found in 1966 that most of the colour of gem opals is derived from these heavily faulted zones; when fragments of perfect, unfaulted material were examined, they were found to be much less colourful and relatively uninteresting as compared with the faulted pieces.

It is anticipated that the weak colour-play of sunflash opal, which needs a bright light source to reveal any colour at all, could be a direct result of an unfaulted, regular array.

Thus really perfect opals are not so perfect after all, for the more structural faults a gem contains, the more colour it may show and so the more valuable it may be. Lattice imperfections result when the perfect, periodic arrangement is out of sequence in a multitude of microscopic regions in the opal. In fact, the best gem opal would have several millions of such imperfections to each cubic centimetre. Just how and why these imperfections occur is a good question to answer after we know why the silica settles out as an array in the first case, rather than always forming a disordered mass which is all that potch is.

Why should the silica particles pack together as spheres of uniform size in regular arrays containing random faulting? These particles of silica aggregate spontaneously in order to reduce the silica–water interface, in much the same way as you can reduce the skin–air interface of your hand by clenching your fingers to make a fist. These aggregates congregate further, layers or shells building around a central nucleus, with each sphere in contact with as many adjacent spheres as possible. When they reach a critical size they tend to settle out of solution and concentration increases at the bottom, to form a gel.

The mixture of solid particles of sub-microscopic sizes in water constitutes what is known as a colloid or sol, and it is the viscosity of the sol which controls the size that the particles must reach before they begin to settle out. In this way uniformly sized particles tend to settle and collect into regular arrangements.

If the sol contains particles of different sizes, particles which are either smaller or larger than the average, they will not fit as perfectly into the growing uniform array of the structure, and unless a particular particle colliding with the surface of the structure is held with several points of attachment, its inclusion is less favoured. Spheres of like size, therefore, tend to fit into a growing structure, but we can see how very simple it is for distortions and so faulting to occur with odd-sized particles.

In nature, precious opal was formed from silica aggregations which developed in groundwaters trapped in the host rocks, especially in basinal structures and perched water tables over the sediments of central

Australia. This is the probable genetic process. Laterite was developed in Australia as a result of a high groundwater table causing leaching of iron-rich minerals from the sedimentary rocks. This condition was terminated with the onset of arid conditions due to a change in the world's climate; the high water table would then have fallen. The sediments are impermeable clays and porous sandstones, and when the water level fell to a clay horizon, it became trapped. This water must have contained dissolved silica leached from the surrounding strata and concentrated in excess of 100 parts per million.

Some movement of groundwater in a lateral flow is reckoned for, and this would have introduced fresh silica into the system. Water would have been lost by evaporation through permeable rocks and in course of time

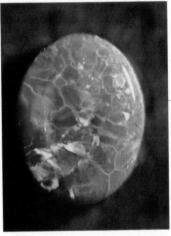

Andamooka crystal opal showing a distinctive hiatus or time-break between subsequent layers of noble opal. The bedding line bisects the triangular stone along its long axis, and the top layer is composed of floral harlequin pattern with red irisations. It is extremely interesting to observe the tapering end into which the bedding lineation extends. It is marked by an incursion of the overlying layer into the bottom, and represents a drag path created by some particle dropping into the still-unconsolidated opal gel during its formation. The particle dropped and dragged out the harlequin patterning into a peacock's tail pattern in the immediate vicinity, and extended that down into the blue-green gel beneath it (C. Totterdell collection, Parramatta, N.S.W.)

Crazing in black opal does not destroy the beauty of this magnificent specimen from Lightning Ridge, but it does have a disastrous effect on the specimen's value. This sample from Lightning Ridge has a harlequin flag pattern, reflected by the boundaries of the crazing flaws. Crazing is considered to be due to an excessive moisture content in opal, greater than 10 per cent by weight, which causes instability in the gem and cracking ensures. Opal can be stabilised by reducing the high water content to within 3–10 per cent (L. Nock collection, Canberra)

the silica developed would have formed a sol and then a colloidal gel. There are many factors involved in this process, or processes. These include the pH of the water, the temperature gradient, and the permeability of the overlying rock. It is considered that the natural rate of deposition of precious opal is only one centimetre's thickness in five million years at a depth of forty metres.

The solidification of the gel was the next phase to occur. This is considered to have developed during the last one to two million years. The opal remained soft and uncemented for long periods before becoming hardened, as is evidenced by the inclusions frequently found which have actually fallen into and through the soft sol. Dessication and cementation finished the material into a hardened mineral, but not without hazard. If too much cementation took place, then the diffracting voids could be eliminated by infilling. And if there are many irregularly arranged spheres, or spheres distorted during drying out, they may distort so many of the voids that they then will no longer have the ability to diffract light; they will merely scatter it, diluting the fire and making the stone look milky, or white.

It is interesting to note that cottoning, an undesirable change seen in some Indonesian and Mexican noble opal, is probably the result of distortion occurring, after mining, in the substance of the opal. Something disrupts the sphere arrangement, and a cotton-ball-like 'growth' appears within the polished piece. A similar phenomenon is noted with some Queensland opal-in-matrix. The highly colourful opal stringers in this ironstone change to become much less fiery, and turn white within a matter of hours after the specimen is opened.

From the above discussion on the causes of opal formation and the origin of colour in opal, it can readily be seen that the application of mineralogical principles in the search for precious opal will greatly facilitate the finding of this remarkable gemstone, and this is the work in which I am currently engaged, as the best proof of a theory is its practical use for the benefit of the public. It is my hope that with the information contained in this book, you too will be able to tell where best you might dig your own opal mine.

QUEENSLAND OPAL

The entire region of western Queensland is one great reservoir of opal. In it lies the precious opal which usually takes the form of iridescent colours permeating brown ironstone matrix. This is beautiful opal, so beautiful, in fact, that many gem authorities regard the best Queensland gems as being even better than the finest pieces of opal to come from Lightning Ridge.

Thanks to the discovery of opal, the Queensland outback was opened up to civilisation. But although many new fields were found, not much work could be sustained. The shortage of water effectively curtailed the best intentions. So even today the opal fields of Queensland are still virtually virgin ground, only briefly worked and scarcely scratched. The country is harsh and imposes its own restrictions; in the past one good season was followed by many when neither man nor beast could live off the produce of the land.

But times have changed, and so have mining methods. Mechanisation has taken over. Water can be transported, roads have been constructed, and working conditions can be made air-conditioned. And in all the thousands upon thousands of square kilometres of parched arid land which blankets the interior of this State, the opal still lies there, waiting, waiting . . .

Here is a mining area larger than the State of Texas, but Queensland opals have yet to be seen throughout the world. Although innumerable opal occurrences have already been reported and classified, there would be thousands yet to be found. But this opal is not so easily obtainable that we can think in terms of mining it as we do coal, for example. The winning of fine opal is always a long task, requiring personal effort and application for which mechanisation will never be a substitute.

The size of these potential deposits gives the world's gem trade the prospect of a source of supply of precious stone for thousands of years hence. Consider the way in which some of the world's finest gemstone areas have become depleted. Burmese rubies from Mogok have been worked out. Kashmir sapphires today are another true rarity. And both diamonds and emeralds occur in finite limited deposits. Compared with

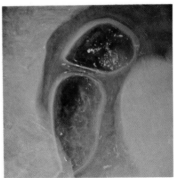

Bubble in opal, Queensland

Brilliant noble opal in a green and red flame pattern infilling cracks in porcellanite—an unusual occurrence, Duck Creek, Queensland (The Mining Museum of N.S.W., Sydney)

this, the expansiveness of the Queensland opal fields offers security to the continuance of the natural precious-stone trade, for as long as man admires beautiful things and continues to admire beautiful opals, then Queensland opals will receive their great share of his attention.

Up until the time when Queensland opal was discovered at Listowel Downs in 1872, all opal then known was volcanic in origin—that is, it was found in the gas vesicles of lava rocks. The opal at Listowel Downs was *sedimentary* opal—that is, opal formed in the cracks and crevices of sedimentary rocks. This sedimentary opal proved to be different from that of all previously known opal deposits throughout the whole world, and was found to occur in many forms—as pipe opal, opal-in-matrix, opal replacements of fossil casts, opal nobbies, opal veins, opal in porcellanite, and as opal cement bonding the grains of the host rock.

Some of these opals are remarkable in size. Many pieces as large as a man's head have been found in Queensland, and one specimen is said to have been an unbroken slab 1.5 metres long. No wonder it is called *boulder opal*.

In its correct interpretation, however, *boulder opal* is the term used to describe that noble opal which occurs as thin veins and pockets within ironstone concretions. The concretions are truly boulders, and occur

Boulder concretions in situ, with visible opal seams

commonly in sandstone and less commonly in mudstone sediments. These boulders are natural concretions, and vary greatly in shape from small spherical bodies less than one-third of a metre in diameter to elongated forms up to three metres in length. These ironstone concretions may not show any opal on the outside, but if they occur within the *opal level*, they may contain some opal inside, deposited in radial or polygonal shrinkage cracks. The boulders have been formed from multiple, iron-rich concentrations, which appear as concentric bands in sectional view.

These concretionary boulders vary in texture. Some consist throughout of concentric bands of hydrated iron oxides; others have a core of sandstone which may contain only specks of iron oxides, or none at all. Opal found in association with such sandstone is commonly referred to as *sandstone opal*, and as a general rule it may be taken that the ironstones yield the deeper tinted and the sandstone the lighter hued stones.

It is only now that the market is coming to accept boulder opal. The first samples found were mostly so thin that the cut stones were very flat or else had to be made up with their natural backing of matrix or rock. Such departures from accepted fashion the market was not at first educated to accept, even for the sake of the brilliant colour. In time such gems did come to be accepted, but only after the sandstone opal had won its way into the hearts of the American people and had been recognised by them as being infinitely superior to the ordinary milky-white Hungarian stones.

Much of this boulder opal has an opaque, dullish yellow, dirty appearance and is completely worthless. Some of it, however, is the most beautiful opal known. Although it may occur as just films and scales of fiery colours against deep brown matrix, we can find the deepest reds, and the richest violets, with spangles of shining ultramarine, pale turquoise, and glittering sea-green specks.

Such opal is of incomparable beauty. It is dreamily lovely. You can see, captive in a little piece of stone, sunsets from Turner's brush, and illustrations of the rapt visions of the poet Keats. Only now are such pieces being shaped into use for pendants and rings, their natural fracture surface forming the uppermost face of the stone, it being far too thin to touch to the lapidary's wheel.

The form of Queensland opal best cut and most appreciated by the Americans in the early days was the sandstone variety known as *pipe opal*. This form demands special notice. It occurs as solid masses, usually drawn out and rounded like finger buns. On the average these pipes are about 125 millimetres long by 25 millimetres wide, and 12 millimetres thick, and often are to be found completely infilled with pure precious opal. The name *pipe* is derived from the cylindrical occurrence of this form of opal.

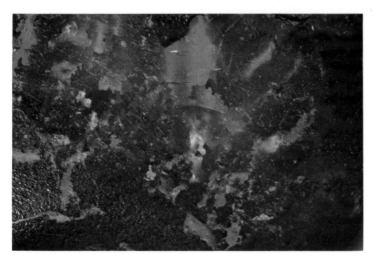

Specimen of boulder opal showing the iron-stone base with the opal veneer in brilliant harlequin patterns (Percy Marks collection, Sydney)

It is the most valuable of all Queensland opal varieties, because each pipe is usually of consistent quality throughout and can be cut into a number of matching gems without the risk that some will be of inferior colour or quality.

These pipes occur both horizontally and vertically in the sedimentary strata of the various Queensland opal fields. Such pipes, variably considered as fossil tree-roots, are actually *rhizo-concretions*, nothing more than natural ironstone concretions with an appearance similar to a root.

It was with this solid sandstone opal that Wollaston won his successes on the London market during 1889. These pipes were nearly always thick enough to cut into well-shaped high-domed cabochons of pure true opal, and this is why it gained such popular favour. Our illustration shows the reason why. It is a piece of superb pipe opal. It is a clear wine-yellow colour through which swim scores of clearly defined large spangles of shining blue, green, orange, and red. This opal is a miracle of condensed beauty. It makes the centre stone for a rare and precious jewel set with large diamonds.

Pipe opal in a setting of diamonds

Another form of opal found in Queensland is called opal-in-matrix. This is a particular form of opalised ironstone and does not refer to any matrix or source of the opal, nor is it even remotely similar to the Andamooka opal matrix. Opal-in-matrix is a dark-brown ironstone concretion, generally small as compared with the ironstone boulder type, in which myriads of tiny cracks have developed in a three dimensional

94

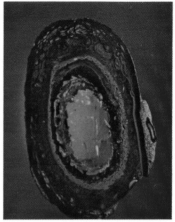

Opal-in-matrix, Yowah Opal Field, Queensland, showing minute synaeresis voids in ironstone concretions infilled with brilliant noble opal (F. Tyne collection, Kurrajong, N.S.W.)

Yowah nut, Yowah, Queensland. The hollow interior of the ironstone concretion has been infilled with noble opal (The Mining Museum of N.S.W., Sydney)

Underground inspection of the Yowah nut band

network, and into them veinlets of brilliant flashing opal have been deposited. The appearance is like tiny threads of glorified gossamer, or like thin films of glaze, on the ironstone. When polished, this ironstone makes up as part of the finished stone, so it is important that the host material be hard enough to polish as well as having sufficient opal to be attractive.

Another remarkable form of Queensland opal is the *Yowah nut*. The nut, as it is called, is a small hollow ironstone concretion, which may be filled with a solid core or kernel of opal. When this is precious opal, a magnificent gem may be obtained. Yowah is the locality where these nuts were first found, and mining for them is still carried out commercially. However, they have been found on occasion in other Queensland opal fields. Sometimes these nuts are empty, at other times they are filled with a white powder, and sometimes water is found in them.

The following is an alphabetical listing of the regions of western Queensland where precious and noble opals have been found or at which mining is reported:

Aladdin Opal Mine
Barcoo River
Black Gate Opal Field
Blackall
Bulloo District
Bull's Creek Opal Mine
Cunnamulla Mineral Field
Cunnamulla Opal Mine
Dirranbandi
Duck Creek
Durham Downs
Elbow Opal Field
Emu Creek Opal Mines
Eromanga Opal Field
Eulo Queen
Exhibition Mine
Fiery Cross Opal Field
Greenflash Opal Mine
Hausington Opal Mine
Hayricks Opal Mine
Horse Creek Opal Mines
Hungerford
Jundah Opal Field
Keeroongooloo Run Opal Field

Koroit Opal Field
Kyabra Opal Field
Kyeenee Opal Field
Kynuna Opal Field
Listowel Downs Opal Occurrence
Little Wonder Opal Mine
Longreach
Lushington Opal Mine
Lyndon B. Johnson Opal Mine
Mascotte Opal Mine
Mayneside Opal Deposits
Mount Tighe
Muttaburra
Noella
Opalton Mineral Field
Opalton Opal Field
Opalville
Paroo Mineral Field
Peppin and Webber's Opal Mine
Pride of the Hills Opal Field
Quart Pot Creek Opal Field
Quilpie Area
Scotchman Opal Mine
Sheep Station Creek Opal Mine

Stonehenge	Windsor Mineral Field
Stoney Creek Opal Mine	Winton
Thargomindah	Yaracca
Valdare Opal Mine	Yellow Nell Opal Mine
Windorah	Yowah Opal Field

There are several mines in the Cunnamulla Mineral Field. Again in alphabetical order, these include:

Bando Opal Mine	Halloway's Opal Mine
Bando Opal Occurrence	Koroit Opal Field
Bingara Opal Prospects	Kyeenee Opal Mine
Black Gate	Moolya Opal Prospect
Elbow Opal Field	Opal Prospects (near Kyeenee)
Elbow Opal Prospects	Yowah Opal Field

Opal has been mined in the Cunnamulla Mineral Field principally from the Koroit and Yowah Opal Fields. Up until 1912 opal worth £14,450, representing 8·38 percent of the total Queensland production, was mined from this district. Today this quantity of precious opal would be worth at least $1 million.

In the early days at the Duck Creek Field, one man is said to have found opal worth £27,000 in three years, and all from the one mine. That same opal today would be worth $2 million dollars on the wholesale market. These deposits at Duck Creek cannot be said ever to have been properly examined, let alone expertly exploited. Fabulous treasure still awaits the scientific searcher at this locality!

There is so much opal in Queensland that it can be found on the surface waiting to be picked up. One prospector and his companions at the beginning of this century traversed the continent from north to south and from east to west on bicycles. They were convinced that there was no other way of accomplishing thorough prospecting. On their search around Cooper's Creek, in the far west of Queensland, they found vast quantities of opal lying on the top of the ground. It was to be seen shining through the boulders and scintillating in the sunshine. But alas for them, this exposed opal was suncrazed and cracked from exposure. Further, the boulders were too heavy to be removed on bicycles alone, and the nearest railway terminated hundreds of kilometres away at Cunnamulla. All western Queensland is rich in opal of some grade, and it is supposed that further out or deeper down even more exists, ready to set the rocks ablaze with blood-red flashes.

Apart from Cunnamulla, there is one other township of Queensland's far west which is the centre of many opal-rich areas. This is Eromanga. So fantastic was the opal production here that the town has been called *Opalopolis*, the city of opals. But today, it is just a poor little town which gives no suggestion that it has seen any better days.

Around Eromanga forty-seven different opal workings are known, and of these the remarkable Aladdin, Stoney Creek, Quart Pot, and the Little Wonder could, perhaps, be considered the principal workings so far. An alphabetical listing of those occurrences at Eromanga will be of interest.

Aladdin Mine
Aurora Borealis Mine
Black's Mine
Boondook Bore Opal Mine
Breakfast Creek Mines
Brown's Last Chance
Bung Bung Mine
Coleman's Cave Mine
Coonavalla Mine or
    Cunnavulla Mine
De Lazra's Mine
Exhibition Opal Mine
Federal Mine
Fish Ponds
Four Mile Mine
Friday Mine
Gem Opal Mine
German Gully
Gladstone Opal Mine
Gooseberry Mine
Hammond's Mine
Hausington Opal Mine
Hen's Nest Mine
Hot Bore Mines
Laman's Mine

Little Wonder Opal Mine
Lucky Day Opal Mine
McGeorge's Opal Mine
Malone's Mine
Mascotte Opal Mine
Mat's Hard Mine
Monte Carlo Mine
Mulcahy's Mine
New Area, Little
    Wonder District
Peppin and Webber's Mine
Pitt's Mine
Pott's Opal Mine
Quart Pot Creek Opal Field
Scanlan's Mine
Scotchman Mine
Stanley's Mine
Stoney Creek Opal Mine
The Gap
The Pinnacles
Two Jacks Mine
Union Mine
Unknown Prospect,
    Federal Area
Yellow Nell Mine

Another extensive opal field within the Cunnamulla Mining District is to be found at Paroo, and from this region came the exquisite blue opal which was so much admired overseas during the 1890s. The principal mining centre was at Duck Creek, but the Emu Creek and Lushington Opal Mines figured significantly. Strangely enough, the region produced continuously for only a single year between 1894 and 1895, although it had been intermittently worked since about 1891. The annual yield fluctuated thereafter, and by 1901 was down to only £450.

The mines known in the Paroo Field are:

Big Creek Opal Occurrences	Goldonga Mine
Brodies Flat	Goodman's Flat
Brodies Hill	Johnson's Mine
Coperella	Lushinton Opal Mine
Duck Creek Opal Field	Never Never Opal Mine
Emu Creek Opal Field	Pride of the Hills
Fiery Cross	Sheep Station Creek Opal Field

Many more extensively worked regions are to be found north from Cunnamulla, and these include the Horse Creek district in the Fermoy or Opalton Opal Field. The oldest known mine here, Cragg's Mine, was probably worked as early as 1888, and several other places are known. The complete list is:

Ann Sharon	Katy's Claim
Carlyle's	King Hit
Cragg's Mine	Mayneside
El Dorado	Norah
Ellen	Pearl
Ellena	Poison
Enterprise	Ruth
Faythe	Susanna

However, within the Opalton Mineral Field, many other deposits are to be found, scattered reminders testifying to the excitement of years gone by in this region, more remote then than today. In alphabetical order, these opal occurrences are listed as:

Cathua	Opal Creek, Maneroo
Corrikie Creek	Opal Creek, Stonehenge
Davenport Downs	Opal Range
Dyson's Mine	Parkdale
Elvo	Ryde (Mount)
Fairview (Mount)	Silsoe Creek
Franklin	Tomkins Mine
Hills Range	Tommy Dodd Mine
Jundah Opal Field	Tankaro
Lyndon B. Johnson Opal Mine	Thomas Mountains
Magic Mine	Tully Range
Mick's Mine	Vergemont
Opal Creek, Mackunda	Warbreccan, (Mount)

Much activity has been centred around Opalton. Early in 1899 an extremely large block of opal, 38 centimetres wide and 3·35 metres long, was found. It may have been a tree trunk completely opalised. At that time it raised an offer of £60,000. Today, as a unique specimen, it would be absolutely priceless. But the miners smashed it up to get it out and to test it for quality!

There is not much prospecting for opal being done in the Opalton Mineral Field today. indeed there is not much in the whole of Queensland. But even though the only opal being produced at Opalton now is the specks and potch picked up by tourists and rockhounds, we cannot consider that the field has been played out. Opalton has been worked, abandoned, reopened, and again deserted in the eighty years of its history, but the hardships which the remoteness of the area imposed upon anyone daring to look for opals here in the early days no longer exist.

The most northern of all the Queensland opal regions, and the most remote, is the Windsor Mineral Field. The principal mining centre is found at Kynuna, but little work has been carried out. Other scattered opal occurrences are known, too, and are tabulated below.

Arizona Station	Lawson Hills
Benduck Tank	Middleton
Blue Speck Opal Mine	Mount Cathedral
Carter's Range	Opal Den Opal Mine
Dagworth Opal Prospect	Red Flame Opal Mine
Kynuna	

It is probable that most of these occurrences will never be worked commercially, for they are so remote. It is not only the comforts of civilisation that miners miss, but also the availability of machinery, fuel, labour, water, and food supplies and services, which all play a role in modern-day prospecting. Of course, it must be realised, too, that these attributes of civilisation are to be had in many other places at opal-bearing localities in central Queensland.

Perhaps the most central town in Queensland's opal belt is Quilpie. Quilpie is itself another busy outback town, but around it are sixteen different known opal deposits, including the Hayricks, which would be the most worked opal mine in Queensland. These localities are:

Barry's Mine	Hayricks Opal Mine
Boulder Opal Prospect	Marble Arch Opal Mine
Bowra Creek	Moble Opal Prospect
Bull's Creek	Mongarlo Opal Prospect
Canaway Opal Occurrence	Red Flash Opal Mine
Depazzie Mine	Sandstone Prospect
Galilee Mine	Valdare Opal Mine
Green Flash Opal Mine	Winbin Opal Occurrence.

Of these, the Hayricks Mine is indeed notable. It is located halfway up the face of a large and striking sandstone mesa, Mount Canaway, and was not discovered and worked until 1930, by Joe Knehr. The output was not constantly great, and Knehr left it in 1933 to look elsewhere. Doing less profitably around the Valdare region, he returned to prospect the Hayricks again in 1935. Others worked the region in a desultory and primitive way for some time, and finally the mine was left to lie idle until 1946. In April of that year, the Hayricks Black Opal Mine Syndicate decided to re-open the mine, which the members believed could produce payable quantities of precious opal.

A lease was taken out, a road constructed right up to the adit, and a water catchment constructed. Mining operations commenced and some magnificent opal was taken out. A fully timbered shaft over 122 metres deep was sunk, and this undoubtedly would be the deepest opal shaft in all Australia, but it could have gone 120 metres beyond the target horizon, for opal has not been formed at such great depths in this country.

Many drives were made, and the soft sandstone and easy rail method of dumping mullock downhill helped progress enormously. The opal was of the sandstone opal variety, occurring in boulders developed within the light grey sandstones, which were found separated by distances of perhaps one metre.

When mined, these boulders were taken to the splitting shed, where they were examined closely. In section, a typical opal-bearing boulder is composed of concentric bands of deposited iron oxides which usually have the best-quality opal at that end or side which was to be found lowermost *in situ*. Contraction in these concretions from dehydration developed numerous syneresis cracks, especially around the peripheral parts and from the centres, extending to surface.

The opal has developed in these cracks and fissures. Only some of it is precious, the rest being potch. The extent of opal deposition varies and, as at other boulder-opal occurrences in Queensland, some boulders were mined in which the opal was completely absent, while others were found to have thick rich veins of it. When only a small amount of opal was present, it usually was of inferior quality. Generally, however, the lower portions of the boulders contain the opal which extends upwards into the rock for various distances, while that deposited in the peripheral fractures is mostly of the precious and noble forms. Usually, that which was found in the central fractures is semi-opal, milk opal, and colourless-to-blue glassy azules type. Successive horizontal layers of colour bandings in vertical veins form an abanderada pattern. or ribbon appearance. There is no set order to the banding, and potch and precious opal can occur in any vertical order.

The syndicate used a diamond saw to split the boulders, as well as the old-time, tried-and-tested method of cleaving the blocks with a tomahawk. With the diamond saw it was possible to separate the fine opal, not as veneers on two pieces of rock but as veins which could be cut and polished. This opal was marketed in the early 1950s as some of the most outstanding opal mined in Queensland. It had a special brilliance which seemed to catch the light, and there was none of the milkiness which characterises the opals more commonly found. The reds, blues, and greens of these fine stones have a special fire which makes them almost alive and scintillating in a riot of colour.

However, now the Hayricks Syndicate has stopped mining, and the mine is noted by the Queensland Mines Department as being sporadically worked by the odd prospector.

It is thanks to the hundreds of odd prospectors that opal has been so extensively found and mined in western Queensland. Nor is the occurrence of the gem confined within this one State's borders. It spills over, so to speak, into New South Wales, South Australia, and the Northern Territory. Queensland opal excites the miner and dealer alike. It is unique even among opals, and it is winning praises anew for its glory now, after having been forgotten for so long.

BLACK OPAL

Black opal is a gemstone which most people associate only with Australia. In fact, it is frequently stated that Lightning Ridge in Australia is the only place in the world where black opals are to be found. Wrong! They have been found at several other fields in Australia, including White Cliffs, Angledool, Grawin, Glengarry, and also at Andamooka and Coober Pedy. The black stones from these places do not compare in quality with the best from Lightning Ridge, but another region of northern South Australia, including Welbourn Hill and Mintabie, produces black opals which are quite the equal of the best blacks from Lightning Ridge.

Black opals have been found widely throughout the extensive Queensland fields too, but as with those found on most of the other Australian workings, their occurrence is a rarity rather than of sufficient quality to constitute a supply. The area around Lightning Ridge is the only locality in the whole world which produces a *supply* of black opal gems.

Black opals have been found in other parts of the world too—in Java, for instance, and Virgin Valley, U.S.A. Old reports dating back to the eighteenth and nineteenth centuries record black opals from Hungary and Mexico as well. But there was always some doubt about these early black stones. It was generally considered that they were coloured black artificially, in much the same way as some agate was cleverly stained black for use as onyx in the trade. Other tricks were used to treat opals, more especially the highly transparent Mexican opals. They were mounted on multi-coloured tinsel or foil, or over mother-of-pearl, or even with bright pieces cut from a peacock's feather set behind them to improve their colour effects. And transparent Mexican opal was sometimes mounted with black velvet behind it to give it a black appearance.

When black opals were found in Australia in 1903, they had some tough bias to combat, as can be seen. The idea of natural opal being blackened would have been strengthened by the Hungarian *prime d'opale*, or opal matrix, which was stained black as is the Andamooka opal matrix today.

By 1897 clever miners and lapidaries at White Cliffs had developed a way of using coloured opal which was too thin to cut into gemstones, and so unsaleable. They put these pieces to good use by flattening the back and cementing them to black onyx; thus a two-piece stone could be made artfully from otherwise waste material. This is the first known instance of opal doublet manufacture. These doublets, resembling black opals, were made six years before black opals were found at Lightning Ridge.

It is not surprising then that the first black opals produced at Lightning Ridge did not find a ready acceptance. Who would want to risk buying some new stones which might have been artificially stained, or which might be more of those 'doublet things'?

It was Tully Wollaston, the pioneer of the Australian opal industry, who set out to persuade the market that here was a truly valuable gem. How dull and unresponsive he found buyers to be at first! However, by degrees the rare beauty of the black opal triumphed over the resistance shown, so much so that Wollaston later expressed his amazement that a modern stone should win its way on sheer merit to such a place of honour as that which Black Opal came to occupy among gems.

After opals were found at Lightning Ridge in 1903, black opals were sold in the rough and mostly unfaced, at a price of £1 per ounce. Wollaston was able to discover only one dealer in London who would handle them, and then only in small lots.

In 1906 Wollaston again went to London, and later to America. In New York, one jeweller on Fifth Avenue stimulated the public taste by displaying these new black opals mounted with diamonds on a lavish scale. Other firms adopted the stone too, and by 1910 it was finding a steady and increasing sale.

At about this time another live-wire-in-the-making was establishing himself in Sydney. By 1899, twenty-one-year-old Percy Marks had served his apprenticeship in the jewellery trade and had established his own jewellery business in the city. When these new black opals came to his notice in 1906 he immediately saw a great possibility in these gems and set out to exploit them. He gathered a valuable collection of gems together and displayed them in Sydney. The general public, the jewellers, and the press were unanimous in their praise of the marvellous beauty and variety of these black stones.

For only five shillings, he found he could peg his own claim at Lightning Ridge, sink his own shaft, and mine his own black opals. In 1907 he was mining, but he never met with success in this. Instead, he bought opals. He returned to Sydney with two suitcases packed to overflowing with the most glorious opals he had ever been privileged to see in one lot. But to sell them was not as easy a matter. He found, as had Wollaston, that the public and the trade were uninterested. But he had the gems cut and polished, mounted, and displayed, and called them 'Rare Black Opals, the Gem Novelty of the Twentieth Century.'

He was determined to create a market for them. Every celebrity in the public eye was openly presented with a 'Rare Black Opal' in some form or other. Sousa, the American bandmaster here on a vist, was presented with a very valuable baton made of Australian wood, mounted in Australian gold, and set with 'Rare Black Opals.' Madame Nellie Melba, Australia's famous prima donna, was presented with a bouquet in which was concealed an attractively wrapped gift package containing a fantastic 'Rare Black Opal' mounted in Australian platinum and Australian diamonds. Madame Pavlova, the members of the English Cricket Team, and all the officers of the visiting American Fleet and also of the Dutch Fleet were given souvenir boxes of Lightning Ridge opal. There were many other recipients.

The Duke of Gloucester received a presentation from the Federation of Australian Jewellers. This was a solid, fiery black opal in a gift box made of solid slabs of pure harlequin-pattern white opal, with mountings of Australian gold. The whole, with an additional matching diamond-studded tie-pin, was presented in a display case of Australian timber.

In 1908 Marks exhibited black opal at the Franco–British International Exhibition in London. He endeavoured to present to Queen Alexandra the most glorious black opal of his collection. The Queen, although admiring the jewel, declined by letter to accept it on account of the rules of court etiquette. The piece weighed fourteen carats, and was reputed to have been the finest example of black opal found to that time. It was then known as the Queen Stone, and subsequently was bought by one of the nobility.

Marks' approaches to the London jewellers and gem dealers met with no immediate success, but he circularised the aristocracy, and they gave him a fair response. They bought the unmounted stones and then took them to their jewellers to have them set. It was only then that the jewellers realised that these new opals were becoming popular and began to make enquiries as to where they could obtain them. This was the beginning of the market for black opals in England.

Another major exhibit was the Panama Exhibition in San Francisco in 1915. Marks was invited to represent the Australian gem industry there, and his display of opals won the Grand Prix by the unanimous vote of the International Jury of Awards.

The rare black opals of Lightning Ridge were having some important effects overseas. They were by now becoming a world-wide advertisement for Australia in general, and New South Wales in particular.

*   *   *

We must now consider what black opal is. In normal opal, the body or ground colour of the stone is practically colourless or white; that is, if the dazzling colour play were totally eliminated, you would have only a white stone—white potch, for instance. In the same way, if the dancing colours of precious black opal were quenched, the stone itself would be a dull black. It was necessary to distinguish this new form from the white opal which had been known for centuries. It was most obviously opal, and the body colour was undeniably black. Wollaston says that it seemed both simple and accurate to call it *black opal*. It has been a good name, and it has stuck.

But how can we convey any adequate description of the startling colour-play which a lovely black opal shows off to anyone who has never been fortunate enough to see one of these top gems? The colours have the full brilliant intensity of the spectrum and they change with the slightest movement, which makes their character intensely interesting. These remarkable patterns can be seen in even a small stone.

White opal has a radiancy about it which is strangely restful. The colour patterns may be similar to those found in black opal, but the white by comparison is quietly beautiful. This property is highly regarded by some people, for there is a simple purity that emerges from the orderly, softened arrangements of colour play.

On the other hand, the colours in black opals seem to spring to life with an astonishing range of brilliant hues that often defy description. It is possible, of course, to categorise such gemstones into our pattern system, but this is solely on account of their dominant features, rather than because they exhibit any rigid and unyielding sameness of design.

Wollaston describes the colour play of bright black opal as 'gleeful spear-thrusts, the broken shining pathways of seraphic order struggling out of chaos; celestial light, imprisoned through the centuries—panting to be free.'

These gems evoke a strange emotion in many people as they see the flashing colours, painted scenes of Antarctic light, volcanic uproar, and lakes of molten colour. In one square centimetre of this opal all the brightest hues of spectral light can be crowded together in the most mysterious ways, set against a background of black night, opaque and dense. These colours appear to be much more brilliant when seen glowing from the black opal rather than from the more ordinary colourless medium. '

How black is black opal? Jet black is one form, the only form at first considered. But deep grey is also recognised by the adjective. And there are lessening degrees of blackness, known as *half-castes* and *quarter-castes* in the old but outmoded terminology.

Such exactness becomes too inflexible to apply, and opal gems if black or very dark grey are all called *black*, whereas dark opals which are not too dark, are known as *semi-black*. Any opal lighter in tone than semi-black opal is regarded as a form of light opal.

But we need a descriptive definition of black opal.

Black opal is that naturally occurring one piece or solid opal which is jet black to dark greyish-blue or deep brown in colour, and absorbs most white light impinging on it and reflects only a minimum. As a consequence, all optical diffraction effects are much more brilliant because of the sharp tonal contrast.

Black opal, a gemstone which has had an important effect overseas as a product of Australia, requires this precise meaning so that the quality of this gem can be meaningfully established. Sometimes off-coloured white opal has been passed off to a visitor as being black opal!

These following points can be considered in the problem of recognising a genuine black opal:

(i) Black refers to the body colour of natural, solid, precious opal. A clear transparent layer of precious crystal opal naturally formed on black potch opal may transmit that base's darkness through its own substance and so assume the quality of being black. This is black opal, too.

(ii) Black Opal is not a term applicable to matrix opal, whether naturally black or artificially stained, nor to Queensland boulder opal.

(iii) No opal doublet should be described as black opal, even though the veneer of noble opal may have come from a black opal.

(iv) The categories of black, semi-black, and light-to-grey opal cannot be infexibly defined. When does a stone grade from black to semi-black? Your commonsense can dictate this and, if in doubt, put it in the lighter category.

Why, we might ask, is black opal black? The reason for blackness in volcanic opal is the presence of impurities of iron oxides, scattered like fine dust through the substance, in sufficient quantity to impart a jettiness of colour. Black opal from Lightning Ridge has carbon along the pseudo-crystalline boundaries. The base colour of white opal is a property of the structural imperfections in the stacking arrangements of the basic silica microspheres that compose opal; these imperfections scatter and diffract white light. Black opal absorbs most of the white light which impinges upon it, save for that fraction which is diffracted as glorious colours.

Black opal from Lightning Ridge is invariably found as small nobbies or nodules, mostly less than three grams in weight. The largest piece of black opal recorded was found in 1907. It weighed 2·2 kilograms. Most pieces, however, cut into gems weighing from a quarter to one carat each.

It is well to realise that a really perfect black opal of any size is exceedingly rare and, it is fairly safe to assert, will become increasingly valuable as opal increases, continually, to win esteem.

There are many superb pieces of black opal which have been named. The Butterfly, Pandora, the Pride of Australia, and The Flamingo are a few. These are the exceptional pieces, of superb quality and perfection, and generally of large size but not necessarily so. To name a stone, the owner simply gives it a suitable title. There are no registrations necessary. An index of named stones is now being compiled by Ellis Ryan of Inland Trading, Coonamble, New South Wales, and this will prove the basis of a catalogue of famous Australian opals. It is to be desired that recognition be given to all superb opals in this way, but not all superb opals are given a name on account of the resultant publicity which may prove adverse for the owners.

AUSTRALIAN OPAL MINING

All the known commercial opal deposits in Australia occur within the weathered Cretaceous rocks and sediments of the inland. Opal does occur in other areas but, to date, it has not been found in sufficient quantities to make its recovery an economic proposition. The exposed Cretaceous rocks are over 70 million years old, and such rocks are to be found throughout 500,000 square kilometres across the central part of Australia.

Although he did not know anything about their age, the lone prospector of long ago soon knew which rocks it was necessary for him to look for if he hoped to find opals. All he needed was sharp eyes to cover the ground for traces of tell-tale float. If he was lucky enough, he might have had a camel or a horse, which he could use when the seasons provided a feed cover. If not, he might have had an old bicycle or he might have just been on foot. But, however he travelled, he just kept on looking, blissfully unaware of the great advances in technology that would one day be available.

When fragments were found, shafts were sunk down through the sandstone in the hope or reaching an opal-bearing layer. Then as the shaft grew deeper and rock removal became more difficult, a windlass was used to remove bucketfuls of dirt.

The choice of site for a shaft was usually based on nothing more than the discovery of a few fragments of float near by. Somebody would throw his hat in the air, and at the place where it landed dig a hole down into the earth for thirty metres or so until he struck the opal level. It might take a month of hard work, every day slowly getting closer to the bottom. At last the claystone stratum was struck. Careful! Careful! Scrape away the clay. Chip it out gently. Nothing! Not a thing. Just clay. It's a duffer. Let's sink another hole over there.

And that is the basis of the many mines in Queensland, where each mine is a collection of several shafts. Only a few of them returned opal, and those that did might not have produced opal of much value. It seems that the development of a field was directly linked more to the amount of shaft sinking the men did, than to the quantity or even the quality of the gem opal found. Unless the gem was met with when the shaft had been sunk, so disappointed were those hardy diggers that they seldom had the inclination to drive tunnels out to see if a patch of opal could be encountered close by. But they would move a few metres away and dig down another ten metres. If the same amount of energy had been expended in tunnelling, there was every chance that an opal patch might have been discovered.

Of course, one of the problems with tunnels is what to do with the dirt. In a horizontal tunnel the dirt would have to be shovelled several times to get it back to the vertical shaft so that it could be removed. When the work involved in this horizontal shovelling was more than that of digging another vertical shaft, it would be easier to dig a new shaft.

Unfortunately for them, these men did not understand the geological environment and the factors that influenced opal formation. However, they knew the properties of the dirt which would lend itself to carry opal, and recognised them when they were encountered.

In the search today for productive regions, we must take into account other aspects which have never been considered by people untrained in regional geology. For one thing, much opal has been located in Queensland on regions which would have been islands within a great area of swamps 10 million years ago. Serious prospecting can be reduced considerably by looking at ancient island locations that existed during the Tertiary Time Period.

More real strikes of top-grade gem opal, not low-grade potch and colour, can only be made with a real knowledge of the mode of opal localisation and of its host material. This is not as simple as making a statement in print though. Geological and geophysical work must be applied to determine the substructure of the rocks. Down warp regions can be delineated, and drilling to collect samples on a regular grid pattern is the next job. Trace mineralisation is looked for in the samples, and the results are used to determine the probability of the ground being opal bearing, because such mineralisation is directly connected with regions of high opal content. The results are plotted on a contour map and an area of highest-density contouring indicates the propitious site for conducting an organised mining program.

The finance required for such an organised programme is no more than that required for any mechanised opal mining used today. In this case, however, the area is worked methodically, a geological control is superimposed on the action, and the results are used to select the best directions that driving can take.

This profitable and organised form of search has not been available

110

until now. Formerly, any form of opal prospecting was haphazard. The fact that so much opal was encountered purely by chance indicates the extent of the opal deposits, for such large numbers of opal finds would not have occurred in Australia if there had not been a far greater amount of opal lying there in the ground waiting for someone to stumble across it.

Compare the simplified means of today with the conditions that confronted a prospecting party seventy years ago. They had to be tough men, then. They set out into a land of promise where they hoped to make a fortune with one stroke of their picks. But at its best it was a land of dreary desolation. The sun beat down incessantly by day, with a searing heat, and at night myriads of flying insects made life almost unbearable.

The only thing in their favour was that they needed neither money nor experience to start in this lottery. All the tools required were a pick, a shovel, a bucket, and a rope. But much talk of the ease with which fortunes could be made encouraged gangs of disreputables from the major cities to swarm to the opal areas too. The 'Push' was just such an odious congregation. The real, live 'Wild West' of Australia grew up in full swing, with saloons and gambling dens, stage holdups, and boom towns. The mining men were as varied in their backgrounds as were the fields they dug. A member of the British aristocracy would dig mines with a bullock driver for a workmate, and the Canadian lumberman could be seen digging alongside the man from Oxford. Irishmen and Scotsmen teamed together. And naturally the Australian bushman was about too.

The many mining areas to be seen in western Queensland not only indicate the numerous localities of opal occurrence, but also reflect the great lack of an indispensable commodity—water. A multi-mixed mob of men would work together on a field, all with the one objective—opal. But they could stay only while they had water. In Queensland, whenever they used up their supply, they all had to abandon camp and set out to find more water and more opal elsewhere.

Some may have been mounted on bicycles or camels, or even horses, but most would have had to walk, carrying their own swag. They must have made a strange procession, blazing the mulga in their determined efforts along the watercourses of dried stream systems. The men on foot would have kept to the main channel-ways of the waterless rivers. The cyclists and horsemen detoured widely over the plains, linking up at night with the main party. Here the day's experiences could be recounted. What water holes had been found? How good was the water? Sometimes stones carrying fiery streaks of gleaming opal were picked up from the sand. Water first, opal second! Opal without water could not be worked. Water without opal was of no avail.

When finally water and opal were located together, the demands on the water would at length prove too much for the supply, and the group would once more move on with the dual search for water and surface showings of colour. Until now, opal prospecting throughout Australia has always been dependent upon such surface showings. It was solely on account of their presence that the early prospectors sank their shafts in search of seams of pure opal. Sometimes they struck opal which had no relation to the specimens found on the surface. These had been washed down from areas higher up. But the reason for successful finds in so many cases is that there may be several levels of opalisation. And where one is found, there certainly could be more. Usually it will be found that only one series has been worked.

No wonder the opal country of Australia is practically untouched. The rocks alternate between coarse sandstone and fine, muddy shales. You can readily see them in the opal mines as you descend. The shales have been weathered into a fine, soft clay, and they form the level, or dirt—the opal level or opal dirt, that is. The opal level is generally only about one metre thick, but may be less or more. In most cases the opal level is within twenty metres of the surface, as this represents the limit for groundwater percolation and evaporation to be effective in the formation of opal.

Usually the most opal and the best opal is found at the top. It is possible, however, to find gemstones even at the very base of the stratum, or through it. These levels, one overlying another, run for extensive distances, with breaks here and there. They represent the successive catchment areas of lakes or lagoons—the bottom of the water-fill into which the fine sediments have settled. Such discontinuous levels are to be found throughout the centre of the country. If you continue mining, sinking your shaft deeper and deeper, you will find a repetition—levels and sandstones, levels and sandstones. But most likely, only the top five of these will prove to contain opals.

Probably the level will be barren white clay when you bottom upon it. Then you tunnel through it. In the old days the miners had no option but to keep on tunnelling, or driving, hoping to find the opal, trusting to see some encouraging signs. Today, they still do the same. They should be doing something different. It is time for a change to modern means!

An opal miner's claim is rectangular. His main shaft should be sunk in the centre of the claim and then he should drive out in four directions, one at a time, to each corner. By so doing he is simplifying his exploration, because any of the continuous formations such as slips and strikes, now known to play a role in opal formation, will be encountered if they are there. Once they are found, and there could be several, they then can be driven upon, and all the profitable opal in the claim will be localised. This is far better than to have a hole, find nothing, give up, and find that somebody else comes along later, digs in a different direction and finds a fortune.

As with any other science, you simply have to know how to see things after all the hard work has been done. Organisation is the keynote in opal exploration—knowing the genesis of the gemstone, knowing the geology of the fields, understanding why opal could and could not develop, appreciating the old methods, applying the new, and recording all results!

Some of the old methods did include puddling and drilling. Because surface indications are on the whole very poor, drilling to see if opal fragments could be obtained in the cuttings was an old aid, originally done by winding a drill-rod by hand. It is still carried on, but today a truck-mounted proline drill is far simpler, more economical and quicker to use. Unfortunately, those individuals who have advanced to this level have not understood the benefits of doing this same work on a scientific basis, for grids still are not laid out. All drilling is as random as the old method of throwing a hat for the selection of shaft sites. The results truly are debatable. What are the statistics? They do not exist. There is no data kept to compute. We can only conclude that much opal must exist for any of it to be found at all.

Now we have the Calweld drill. This is a truck-mounted drill which can be rapidly set over most sites and a twenty-metres-deep hole sunk within a few hours. Not only that, but since the Calweld rig sinks a drill hole which is one metre wide, a man can climb down it. Now who would spend a whole month digging a hole when a machine can do it for him in two hours? These rigs are extensively used in opal mining on the Australian fields today. They are cheap to use, cheap to hire, and cheap to operate.

Other machinery available today includes underground mining equipment, automated to reduce hard, slow work. At Coober Pedy and Andamooka a large number of miners are operating negative pressure conveying and separating devices to raise dirt automatically to the surface from underground. Caterpillar earth-moving equipment is used as well for open cutting. In common use are the motorised hoists, automatic winches, compressed-air equipment and dry and wet puddling machines. These puddlers have revived Lightning Ridge and the neighbouring Grawin and Glengarry fields. But their use also requires the availability of large trucks to transport the unprocessed opal dirt to the puddling sites. A wet puddler uses water to sieve the clay, holding back only those lumps, rocks, or opal which will not go through the basket. These machines are mechanically driven, and all the opal dirt can be removed in bulk and processed *en masse*. This means that a modern opal-mining team can treat in one day as much ground as may have been covered in a whole month by arduous, manual effort ten years ago.

113

Within these last ten years open-cut mining has been extensively developed in Queensland and at Coober Pedy, Andamooka, White Cliffs, and Lightning Ridge. This method does work. Opal has been found. But how much more advantageous it would be for the operators if their efforts were made with a systemised control so that results could be kept and used. Mechanisation has added a whole new dimension to the great opal treasure hunt. Open cutting of opal mines, although first used at White Cliffs during the mid-1890s, is probably the grandest scale of opal mining development so far devised. Some cuts are grandiose quarries. Some are merely holes scraped along the ground.

Here I do not intend to delve into the intricacies of the individual machines, nor to compare one with another for effectiveness. Suffice it to give them attention. There are other aspects which must be drawn to the attention of anyone wishing to go opal mining, and especially to visitors to the fields.

The opal fields are remote from each other as well as from main towns and sources of supply. When you prepare to visit them, know that. Carry water always and sufficient petrol and food. In many areas provisions cannot be bought along the road, for no one is there to sell them. The major fields (the famous few) are towns, so you can buy stores there.

Be sure your directions are clear, and let someone know if you are going out looking for a remote, hidden, or forgotten digging. Then, if you become lost, a search party will at least know where to look for you. Men have perished in these environments. Make sure you do not meet the same fate by ensuring that your car is in its best mechanical condition and that you are fully equipped to meet all emergencies.

Opal mining is a decidedly haphazard business. Haphazard because of the unsophisticated way it has been handled. Opal to Australia means tens of millions of dollars annually in export earnings, but it is certainly discouraging to find that the trade is steeped in ignorance that rivals in its effect the old superstition associated with opal. It is to the miners' benefit to know their country and where they will find opal, to eliminate luck so that they can be sure of getting results.

THE VALUE OF OPALS

Our discussion of opal as a gemstone cannot be complete unless it includes a basis for establishing the value of opals, and to understand this we need to realise what exactly makes them valuable.

The real value of opal lies in its being the only gemstone which creates genuine amazement in the human mind. It is not simply a sea of intense blue or green, nor just a piece of encapsulated red. It does not glitter, either. Samples may have these properties, but there is more. Reds can change on a quiver to orange and be suffused with a shower of green, or be blanketed suddenly by a veil of purple. That is opal—an indescribable mixture of spectral hues in everchanging display. How can this play of colour, which is such an indefinable property, be broken down to simple terms so that we can place a value on an opal?

Firstly, the higher the brilliancy of an opal, the higher its commercial worth. If it exhibits pattern in perfection, this greatly enhances its value. The colour play and the uniformity of the pattern determine the extent of demand, and demand creates value. Stones which are most valuable are those that exhibit a fine pattern of bright colours over the whole surface, while inferior pieces have dull colours or uninteresting, unremarkable designs. In the lowest grades a portion of the stone may be marked with dead areas in which potch and not colour is to be seen. But scarcity, demand, and a great awakening to the instrinsic worth of opal have created tremendous interest in this gem, the fifth precious stone. And like other precious stones, size is of importance too. The larger the stone of fine quality, the more valuable it is compared with a smaller one, of course.

We also have background colours to consider. There is black opal, light opal, and fire opal. These are further qualified as jelly, cherry, crystal, white, golden, grey, water, boulder, and matrix. Black opal stands by itself at the top of the list. Then popular demand puts crystal next in line, followed by boulder and white, and then light grey, jelly, water, and finally matrix. Mexican cherry opal and both the sun and aranjado types of fire opal are not commercially displayed in Australia, although they are

115

considered very valuable in both Japan and the United States where they would rank equal to crystal opal. Faceted transparent fire opals as well as golden opals from Australian sources are so rare on the marketing scene that they must be considered collectors' items. It is of course assumed that the colour play and size of each are equally comparable on all points.

Other forms of opal such as hydrophane, potch, and common opal have no commercial worth apart from their value as collectors' items.

Opal is now manufactured synthetically, and this synthetic gem is much more expensive than synthetic ruby or sapphire. It augments the natural supply of precious opal and is of unusually high perfection. The need for synthetic opal reflects a serious underproduction in the natural supply of fine quality opal from all the Australian mines—the annual production cannot meet the natural demand.

Other opals which may be of high perfection and yet are manufactured stones as well include the opal doublet, triplet, and dyed Andamooka matrix. Each looks as if it were fine black opal, but is skilfully made and relatively inexpensive. The very finest may cost only a few hundred dollars each. Their value depends upon their perfection of pattern and colour play, as well as size.

When putting a realistic price on any opal, whether natural, synthetic, or manufactured, the buyer or seller must know the prevailing market prices. Such prices can differ from place to place, from town to town, and from country to country.

In some places a baroque or uneven shape may be more fashionable. Such is the vogue for turquoise in American Indian work. Opals, with the exception of transparent fire opal, are cut *en cabochon*. They need, for best value in Australia, to be even in outline and balanced in design. The best value is always obtained for the shape most in demand, the oval cabochon which has a domed surface. A flat surface is not as valuable as a dome, all else being equal.

In fact, a dome of equivalent weight and appearance to a flat has three times the flat's value.

A factor in the selection of rough opal when buying is consideration of how much wastage will be encountered. The best material is chunky pieces from which gems can be created with a minimum loss. Normally at least two-thirds of the material will be ground away. Professional cutters allow for only thirty percent recovery. The loss for low-grade opal with bars of colour in potch, or oddly shaped pieces which taper and twist, will be much greater still! Naturally, both rough and polished opal must be free from cracks and flaws as well.

Value is subject to personal preference. This is an unpredictable aspect which varies from individual to individual. Anybody not wanting red will hardly be tempted to pay a high price for that colour, but should he be wanting blue, then the seller of blue has an advantage. We can consider that evaluation of gems of opal manifests itself as an extravagant and even ridiculous worship of colour.

To make any attempt to outline the scale of values of colours, we must classify them into some sort of system. The following table indicates a simplified method of doing this: Value decreases down the table.

RELATIVE COLOUR VALUES

Body or Background Colour	Play of Colours (Dominant colour listed first)	Pattern Decreasing value
Black	Red	Harlequin, pinpoint, flash
Black	Red and blue	
Black	Red and green	
Black	Red, green, and blue	
Black	Green and red	
Black	Green, red, and blue	
Black	Green and blue	
Black	Blue and red	
Black	Blue, red, and green	
Black	Blue and green	
Black	Blue	
Light	Red	
Light	Red and blue	
Light	Red, green, and blue	
Light	Red and green	
Light	Green and red	
Light	Green, red, and blue	
Light	Green and blue	
Light	Blue and red	
Light	Blue, red, and green	
Light	Blue and green	
Light	Blue	

An important factor relative to the value of opal, yet one which is unappreciated, is its setting in jewellery and its display. With few exceptions, most opals displayed are of inferior quality set in mountings of mediocre design. It is unfortunate that these are generally the only examples of our wonderful Australian opals that are seen by the public. The gem is not even complemented, and a very poor tribute is paid to the tastes of prospective clients. Such low-grade material is not the only opal available, of course, but it does have such a dominating influence in forming public opinion that the opal industry suffers from it. Yet the *real* opal industry is certainly active in showing first-quality gems; it is the indiscriminate merchant cashing in who demotes this fine gem into an item of kitsch for the tourist trade. Opal will always suffer while some of these people continue to present opal as some second-rate, cheap, costume-jewellery stone.

VALUE OF OPAL AND THE P.R.W. INDICES

How then does one evaluate precious opal? Realising the acute necessity for product promotion, the Lightning Ridge Miners' Co-operative Association has devised a scheme for evaluating black opal. I have adapted this scheme so that all opal can be satisfactorily valued against it. Essentially the plan is to categorise each gem and price it with a scale of indexation. The original P.R.W. indices are used here with the following meanings:

P Index: refers to the Scale of Appreciation, 1–100

R Index: is the intrinsic value per carat. Here it is denoted in Australian dollars as at 31 March 1975.

W Index: is the intrinsic value per carat adjusted in relation to inflation since 31 March 1975.

The following tables present a simplified way of comprehending the many points of appreciation that are involved in valuing precious opal. Value trends around the world vary for opal, but this is not our concern here. The table will show, even to the most inexperienced, a way by which Australians can readily appreciate the finer points of quality Australian opal.

It is important to realise that the system outlined here is a basis for the buyer and seller to arrive at an acceptable price. Once the value W has been calculated, bargaining usually takes over, especially in the case of high-quality stones, with the seller likely to want a rather higher price for a harlequin pattern and possibly less for a pinfire or flash.

118

The P Index—The Scale of Appreciation

Gem Features	Points to be Awarded or Deducted	Notes
Opal Type:		
Black	+30	The P Index is the total after
Black Crystal	+20	adding or deducting all points
Semi Black	+15	scored.
Crystal	+10	
Fire	+10	
Top White	+10	N.B. Cabochon-shaped, oval
Grey	+ 5	or round stones are taken as
Light	+ 5	being basic features; for such,
Boulder	+ 5	no points are awarded.
Prominent Irisation Effects		
Red	+30	
Orange	+15	
Green	+10	
Blue	+ 5	
Indigo	+ 5	
Purple	+ 5	
Red Bonus	+ 6	Awarded if prominent red is immediately followed by prominent blue.
Colour Bonus	+ 5	Awarded if prominent irisation is prominently matched by its complementary colour. See Appendix I.
Pattern		
Size	to+ 4	+1 point for each quarter area of gem face.
Purity	to+ 4	+1 point for each quarter area of gem face.
Brilliance	to+ 4	+1 point for each quarter area of gem face.

Gem Features	Points to be Awarded or Deducted	Notes
Night or Shade Stone	+ 2	Some opal is so brilliant that even in minimum light it is still very spectacular.
Bonus for two of these properties	+ 2	
Trueness	+ 6	No points if the colour extinguishes.
Odd shapes	to − 10	Collectors' items or named stones excluded.
Dead spot on face	to − 40	10 points deducted for each quarter of facial area affected.
Potch in colour or potch lines	to − 20	10 points deducted for each half of facial area so affected.
Cracks	to − 20	10 points deducted for each half of facial area so effected.
Sand or matrix on face	to − 40	20 points deducted for each blemish, even if only as large as a pin head. Above two instances, the piece should be rejected as a gem.
Sand or matrix on back	to − 4	If the basal area has a fine colour play, then deduct one point for each quarter of the area so affected. Otherwise disregard, as such inclusions offer irrefutable proof that the gem is natural.
Flat-faced	÷ 3	Reduce total net points to $33\frac{1}{3}\%$.

R Index

The intrinsic value per carat of the opal is obtained in units of Australian currency as at the quarter ending 31 March 1975, matching the opal's P Index to the R Index.

P Index	R Index	P Index	R Index
1	$0.75	36	225.00
2	1.13	37	262.50
3	1.50	38	300.00
4	1.88	39	337.50
5	2.25	40	375.00
6	2.63	41	412.50
7	3.00	42	450.00
8	4.50	43	487.50
9	6.00	44	525.00
10	7.50	45	562.50
11	9.00	46	600.00
12	10.50	47	637.50
13	12.00	48	675.00
14	13.50	49	712.50
15	15.00	50	750.00
16	18.00	51	787.50
17	21.00	52	825.00
18	24.00	53	862.50
19	27.00	54	900.00
20	30.00	55	937.50
21	33.00	56	975.00
22	36.00	57	1012.50
23	39.00	58	1050.00
24	42.00	59	1087.50
25	45.00	60	1125.00
26	52.00	61	1162.50
27	60.00	62	1200.00
28	67.50	63	1237.50
29	75.00	64	1275.00
30	90.00	65	1312.50
31	105.00	66	1350.00
32	120.00	67	1387.50
33	135.00	68	1425.00
34	150.00	69	1462.50
35	187.50	70	1500.00

P Index	R Index	P Index	R Index
71	1537.50	86	2100.00
72	1575.00	87	2137.50
73	1612.50	88	2175.00
74	1650.00	89	2212.50
75	1687.50	90	2250.00
76	1725.00	91	2325.00
77	1762.50	92	2400.00
78	1800.00	93	2475.00
79	1837.50	94	2550.00
80	1875.00	95	2625.00
81	1912.50	96	2700.00
82	1950.00	97	2775.00
83	1987.50	98	2850.00
84	2025.00	99	2925.00
85	2062.50	100 +	3000.00

Specimen A

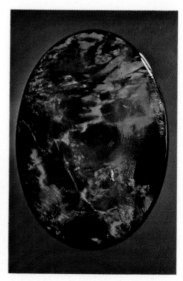

Specimen B

W Index

The value of an opal can now be deduced from the formula:
$$W = X(CR + R),$$
where R is the R Index,

        C is the rate of inflation in Australia since 31 March 1975 to the time of writing, expressed as a percentage,

        X is the weight in carats.

Examples:

Gem Features	Specimen A 7 cts Flash of Fire White Opal	Specimen B 19.5 cts Scotch Plaid Black Opal
Black		+ 30
Top White	+ 10	
Orange prominent	+ 15	
Green prominent		+ 10
Blue prominent		+ 5
Colour Bonus	+ 5	
Pattern Size	+ 3	+ 4
Pattern Purity	+ 2	+ 4
Pattern Brilliance	+ 2	+ 4
Bonus	+ 2	+ 2
Trueness	+ 6	+ 6
Dead Spot	− 10	
Total P	35	65

Indices	Specimen A 7 cts Flash of Fire White Opal	Specimen B 19.5 cts Scotch Plaid Black Opal
R Index	\$187.50	\$1312.50
C	17.28%	17.28%
X	7 cts	19.5 cts
W (1976)	$7(0{\cdot}1728 \times 187{\cdot}5 + 187{\cdot}5)$ $= \$1539.30$	$19{\cdot}5(0{\cdot}1728 \times 1312{\cdot}5 + 1312{\cdot}5)$ $= \$30\,016.35$

123

These indices display the intense thought and consideration which are needed for the effective marketing of top-quality opal. They represent a marked advance for the opal-mining industry, not only of Lightning Ridge but for the whole Australian trade. The outstanding aspect of the P Index is the manner in which points are allotted. A stone can earn points only if it is really good, and loses them rapidly for seemingly slight imperfections. For instance, a gem can earn only six points if it is genuinely true, but it can lose up to eighty points if it is not completely true.

It can be expected that universal adoption of such a scheme would definitely bring about improved cutting techniques, whereby stones would always be finished for quality and not for size. At all events, such standards would promote the very best opal and establish a system whereby opal appreciation is lucidly explained for the most avid and demanding collector.

OPALISED FOSSILS

As the sedimentary opals of Australia form in pre-existing cavities of the rocks, it is not surprising to discover that opal can fill casts left by pre-existing fossils. These moulds, or casts, are cavities in the strata and develop after the fossil shell, bone, or wood has been removed after decay by permeating groundwater solutions. It is truly remarkable how exactly these casts preserve in detail the shapes of life forms which existed so many million years ago during the Cretaceous period.

The most common fossils preserved by noble opal are teeth, wood, crinoids, bones, and Pelecypoda and Gasteropoda shells, as well as belemnites. From Idaho in the United States of America, the partly opalised remains of an early form of horse, *Equus protohippus*, have even been found, as well as solid sections of opalised tree-limbs and fir-cones from Virgin Valley in Nevada.

A form of fir tree, opalised by common opal, has been found at White Cliffs. This pseudomorph has subsequently been fractured, and noble opal has been deposited as an infilling along those cracks. But perhaps one of the most remarkable fossils ever to have been unearthed on that field was the completely opalised skeleton of an extinct sea reptile, *Plesiosaurus*. This specimen was only about 1.5 metres long, although Plesiosaurus was distinguished by a very long neck, small head, short body, and tail which, altogether, would have reached a total length of twelve metres in a mature specimen. Opalised vertebrae-joints, ribs, blade-bones, and flippers or paddles were unearthed. Lamentably, even though this fossil had value as a curio, this value was not as great as that of the opal, and it was broken up for sale as gemstones.

Nevertheless, bony fragments of Plesiosaurus have been found at Lightning Ridge and in Coober Pedy and Andamooka, South Australia, as well. Another interesting aspect of these fossils is the preservation in precious opal of the scale armour of some of the lizards. It is as well to pause a moment and reflect upon the conditions that existed in what is now central Australia back in the Cretaceous times. It was not one vast sea, as so many erroneously believe, but an ever-changing braided network of streams and interconnected lagoons, shifting seasonally and dumping sands and muds continuously.

In the salt-water lagoons there were sea-shells. The most common form is that which we call Pelecypoda, the bivalve or mussel type of shell. Univalve shells, a snail-like shell, occur replaced by noble opal too, but are much more rare. Both types have been discovered on each of the main Australian opal fields. Usually opal constitutes the thin shell part, the interior having been filled with mud after the creature's burial from siltation. But sometimes this chamber is completely infilled with precious opal so that the shell is opalised right through, from one valve to the other. This represents that very exceptional case when the animal buried itself into the sediment, and when it died it was not subject to sedimentation.

The wood from White Cliffs has provided some of the most interesting opal pseudomorphs found in Australia. Some of it is very fine in grain and texture, and in many cases it is infiltrated with noble opal of beautiful colour and of secondary origin, infilling cracks.

The first opalised wood reported in Australia was from Queensland. In fact, this is the first place in the world where a fossil in noble opal has been recorded. It was in 1887. The stony material of the specimen was a rich chestnut-brown and quite opaque. The portions of opal were translucent

Wood-boring pelecypods replaced by noble opal within silicified wood, White Cliffs, N.S.W. Scale: patch = 1 cm (Donated by E. Murphy to the Mining Museum of N.S.W., Sydney)

Belemnites replaced by precious opal, Coober Pedy. The cut gems of harlequin pattern light opal indicate the same quality of brilliant fracture-free opal (I. Sykes collection, Melbourne)

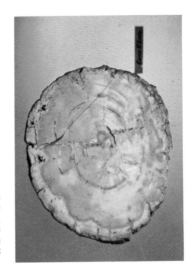

Opalised wood of a fir tree, White Cliffs. Two periods of silicification are evident: first the replacement of the wood by common opal, then the infilling of crevasses radiating from the core by noble opal. Scale: patch = 1 cm (Donated by E. Murphy to the Mining Museum of N.S.W., Sydney)

Ferruginised wood infilling with precious opal (L. Withers collection, Sydney)

and of rich purple, blue, and green colours, cylindrical in form, and traversing the matrix in various directions.

In some instances at least these cylindrical opal pipes were originally formed by embedded stems or other portions of plants. In many cases portions of the vegetable tissue are to be seen completely encased and preserved by the noble opal.

Also from White Cliffs comes the opal *pineapple*. These are not fossilised fruits, but rather are the replacement by opal of pre-existing crystal of a mineral called glauberite. Sometimes these replacements are of gem opal, sometimes opal of inferior quality with blue and green tints prevailing, and in other cases of common milky opal or potch. Long ago, during the Cretaceous period, the glauberite was dissolved and removed in solution. Those open casts were then later filled by opal. And because these replacements have been likened by the early miners to 'fossil pineapples,' they became known locally as such. Of course, they are 'fossil' crystals, or better still, *(precious) opal pseudomorphs after glauberite crystal aggregates.*

Fortunately the Mining Museum of Sydney has a superb collection of

White Cliffs opal pseudomorphs which were left to it by a well known and highly respected opal buyer, Mr Ted Murphy. This collection is probably unique in the world.

Opal fossils are an exceptionally interesting form of mineral and one which you can easily and inexpensively start acquiring to build a unique opal collection.

APPENDICES

Appendix I

THE COLOUR WHEEL

The colour wheel illustrates the range of colours in the spectrum. Each two diagonally opposite hues are complementary to one another. Split harmonies result when one colour is associated with the two nearest neighbours to its complementary, and triadic combinations are formed with hues separated by 120° on the wheel, e.g. red, yellow, and blue.

In opal, extremes of spectral chroma are seen in harmonious relationships—by complementary colours and by means of closely associated hues, split-complementary and triadic hue harmonies, as well as by analogous colour harmony in which only two of the three primary colours are represented, and by monochromatic harmony whereby variations occur in intensity of a single hue.

A valuable and hereto unappreciated factor concerning fine opal is that the colour plays of such gems are within the colour harmonies as set out. Without the complementary relationships, unattractive features become outstanding.

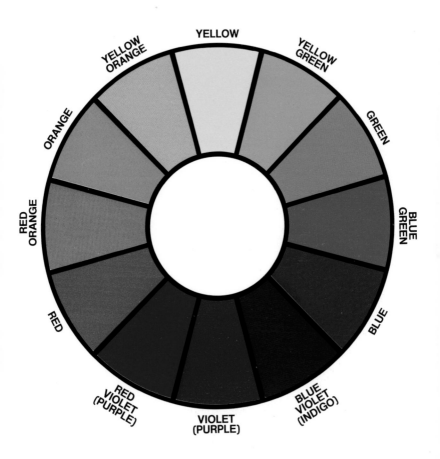

YELLOW

YELLOW ORANGE

YELLOW GREEN

ORANGE

GREEN

RED ORANGE

BLUE GREEN

RED

BLUE

RED VIOLET (PURPLE)

VIOLET (PURPLE)

BLUE VIOLET (INDIGO)

Appendix II

OPAL STRUCTURE

The structure of precious opal is characterised by closest packing of spherical silica micelles. The structures modelled here are the *hexagonal close-packed* and the *cubic face-centred* forms.

The first layer of closest packed spheres occupies site positions designated as A. Each trio of neighbouring spheres in a closest-packed layer provides one hollow, site B, in which a sphere of the next layer above can rest, as is emphasised by the tetrahedron, lower right. There are two different sets of such sites in each closest-packed layer and either set provides all the B sites for spheres in the second closest-packed layer.

This second layer is depicted in the model as three light-grey triangular sets of spheres occupying B sites, all others being omitted for clarity. In like fashion, the second layer forms two different site sets, A and C, relative to the A sites occupied by the first layer. When three neighbouring spheres of the second layer form a site which immediately overlies site A of the first layer, then that site is designated A also. The third layer stacked over sites A, gives an ABABAB ... sequence and hexagonal close packed structures are formed. Correctly, they have seven spheres in the third layer, only one of which is illustrated here, forming the basal pinacoid (0001) of the hexagonal prism. Each hexagonal prism has seventeen and each sphere is itself part of seventeen interconnected prism units. The seventeen spheres form the basic unit of a hexagonal prism, and the prism can develop by its repetition.

When the third layer, however, occupies the set of C sites, the layers are stacked in the sequence ABCABC ... and face-centred cubic forms are developed. The outline clearly depicts a crystallographically oriented cube showing faces with Miller indices (100), (010), and (001). Each isometric unit is composed of 14 spheres, and each sphere forms part of 14 interconnecting cubes.

The tetrahedron is shown lying on a face designated here as (111), the other faces being $(1\bar{1}\bar{1})$, $(\bar{1}1\bar{1})$ and $(\bar{1}\bar{1}1)$. These three latter faces are close-packed planes along which the silica micelles of opal form layers with a wider separation distance between them (one sphere diameter) than have the closest-packed layers. Each (111) type close-packed plane of spheres is now readily recognisable within the hexagonal prism and as the faces on the cube. Each form has three directions in which this type of (111) packing can be determined. Since they do have a full sphere diameter spacing, there is not as strong a bond along their direction as with other directional planes. Slippage can occur along the (111) planes with less interference than along other planes, and fractures can favour the (111) direction also.

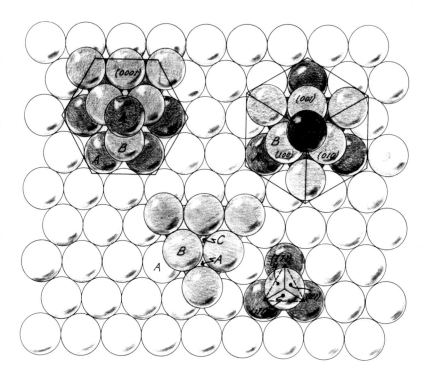

In natural opal such slippage has occurred and parallel lineations within the units of opal colour-play are representatives of steps formed when the soft gel was under stress during dehydration. The strain led to slip which created the parallel structural faults within the perfectly repetitive grain structure of gem opal.

Such plastic deformation along the three (111) planes in opal from Spencer, Idaho, has created a genuine asterism and a six-rayed star opal can be won. A rare star opal from Glengarry, New South Wales, is also illustrated within this text.

Appendix III
OPAL CONSTRUCTIONS
Solid opals have been known since Greek and Roman days. We know that doublets, two-piece opal constructions, were developed at White Cliffs during 1897, but it is probable from what Pliny says, that the Romans made them as well. Triplets, a combination of potch backing, opal veneer, and clear rock-crystal crown, were patented in 1958 by R. V. Marks.

The illustration sets out the basic opal cabochon cuts.

1   Precious Opal
2   Girdle/Setting Edge
3   Noble Opal Veneer
4   Black Cement
5   Potch Backing
6   Rock Crystal Crown
7   Clear Cement

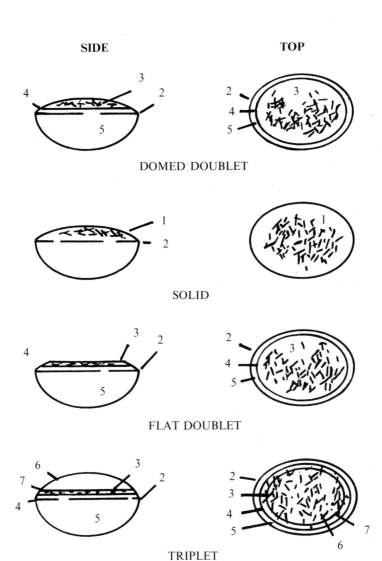

SIDE   **TOP**

DOMED DOUBLET

SOLID

FLAT DOUBLET

TRIPLET

135

Appendix IV

GEOLOGICAL TIME CHART

APP. AGE (m.y.)	ERA	PERIOD	EPOCH	OPAL REFERENCES
	CAINOZOIC	QUATERNARY	RECENT ◄	Opal from Spencer, Idaho formed during recent time
1			PLEISTOCENE	in Late Pleistocene volcanics
13		TERTIARY	PLIOCENE ◄	Australian precious opal
25			MIOCENE ◄	is believed to have formed
36			OLIGOCENE	during this time
58			EOCENE	The Virgin Valley beds were
63			PALEOCENE	deposited
110	MESOZOIC	CRETACEOUS	UPPER	Australian sedimentary rocks containing opal deposited
135			LOWER ◄	during this time
180		JURASSIC		
220		TRIASSIC		
280	PALAEOZOIC	PERMIAN		
345		CARBONIFEROUS		
410		DEVONIAN	◄	Precious opal in Upper Devonian; Mintabie beds, South Australia
425		SILURIAN	◄	Erratic quartzite boulders found at White Cliffs and Andamooka developed during this period
500		ORDOVICIAN		
600		CAMBRIAN		
1100	PRECAMBRIAN	PROTEROZOIC	◄	Pre-Cambrian rocks form the basement to the sedimentary deposits of Australia's opal fields
2400		ARCHEAN	◄	Ultrabasics containing precious opal from Coolgardie, West. Aust. formed in Archean time
2700				

OLDEST KNOWN ROCKS IN PRECAMBRIAN 3,300,000,000 YEARS

LIST OF MAPS

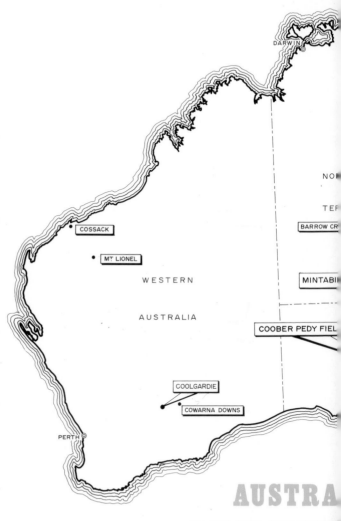

DARWIN

NO[R]

TE[R]

BARROW CR[EEK]

MINTABI[E]

COOBER PEDY FIEL[D]

COSSACK

MT LIONEL

WESTERN

AUSTRALIA

COOLGARDIE

COWARNA DOWNS

PERTH

AUSTRA[LIA]

MAJOR OPAL OCCURRENC[E]
OPALIFEROUS AREAS (i.e. C[...]

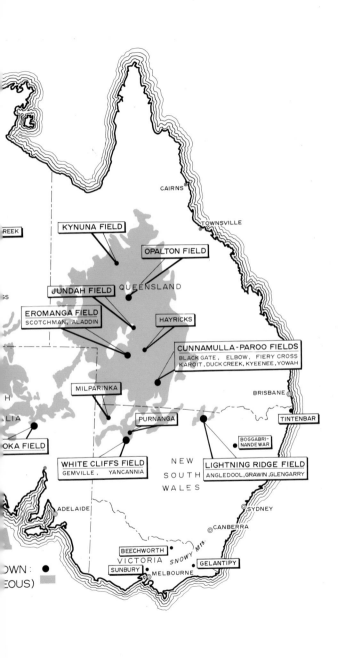

CAIRNS

TOWNSVILLE

REEK

KYNUNA FIELD

OPALTON FIELD

JUNDAH FIELD   QUEENSLAND

SS

EROMANGA FIELD
SCOTCHMAN, ALADDIN

HAYRICKS

CUNNAMULLA - PAROO FIELDS
BLACK GATE , ELBOW , FIERY CROSS
KAROIT , DUCK CREEK , KYEENEE , YOWAH

MILPARINKA

BRISBANE

H

LIA

PURNANGA

TINTENBAR

OKA FIELD

BOGGABRI-
NANDEWAR

WHITE CLIFFS FIELD
GEMVILLE .   YANCANNIA

N E W

S O U T H

W A L E S

LIGHTNING RIDGE FIELD
ANGLEDOOL , GRAWIN , GLENGARRY

ADELAIDE

SYDNEY

CANBERRA

BEECHWORTH

SNOWY Mts.

VICTORIA

GELANTIPY

OWN :

SUNBURY   MELBOURNE

EOUS)

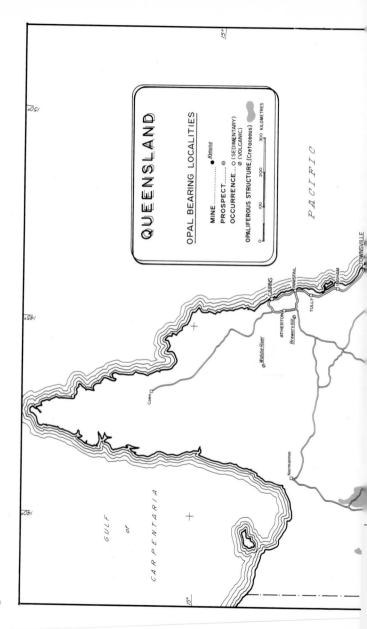

QUEENSLAND

OPAL BEARING LOCALITIES

MINE .... ● *Kynuna*
PROSPECT .... ◎
OCCURRENCE ...... O (SEDIMENTARY)
                  Ø (VOLCANIC)
OPALIFEROUS STRUCTURE (Cretaceous)

0   100   200   300 KILOMETRES

PACIFIC

CAIRNS
INNISFAIL
TULLY
ATHERTON
Brewery Hill
INGHAM
TOWNSVILLE

Ø *Walsh River*

Coen

Normanton

GULF
of
CARPENTARIA

140

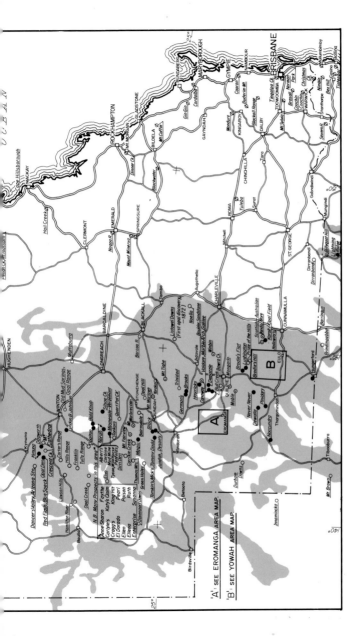

'A' SEE EROMANGA AREA MAP.

'B' SEE YOWAH AREA MAP.

141

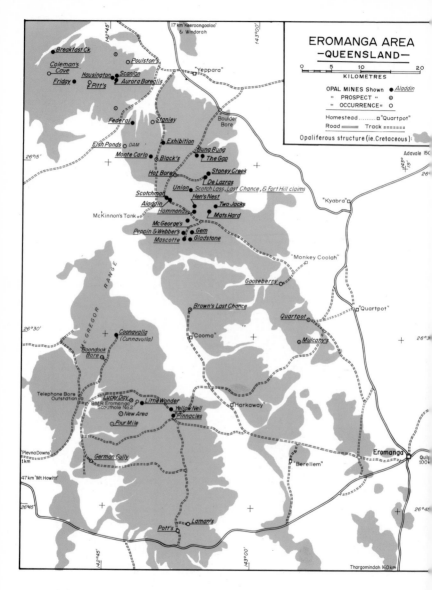

EROMANGA AREA
—QUEENSLAND—

0	5	10	20

KILOMETRES

OPAL MINES Shown ● *Aladdin*
  " PROSPECT " ◎
  " OCCURRENCE" ○

Homestead.........□ "Quartpot"
Road ═══ Track ═════

Opaliferous structure (ie.Cretaceous):

17 km 'Keeroongooloo'
& Windorah

Breakfast Ck.

Coleman's Cave
Hausington
Friday ●   *Pitt's*
Scanlan
Aurora Borealis

Poulston's
"Yeppara"

Federal
Stanley
Boulder Bore

Fish Ponds ○ DAM
Exhibition
Bung Bung
The Gap

Adavale 150

Monte Carlo   *Black's*
Hot Bore
Stoney Creek
De Lazras
Scotchman
Union   *Scotch Lass, Last Chance, & Fort Hill claims*
Aladdin
Hen's Nest
Hammonds
Two Jacks
Mats Hard

"Kyabra"□

McKinnon's Tank ○
McGeorge's
Peppin & Webber's
Gem
Mascotte
Gladstone

"Monkey Coolah"

Gooseberry

Brown's Last Chance

"Quartpot"

Coonavalla (Cunnavulla)

"Cooma"

"Quartpot"

Boondook Bore ○

Mulcahy's

Telephone Bore
Outstation
Lucky Day   *Little Wonder*
BMR Eromanga
Scouthole No.2
◎ *New Area*
Yellow Nell
Pinnacles
Four Mile

"Harkaway"

'Plevna Downs'
1km
German Gully

"Berellem"
Eromanga
Quilp
100k

47 km 'Mt.Howitt'

Pott's
Laman's

Thargomindah 160 km

26°15'
26°30'
26°45'

142°45'
143°00'
143°15'

M^cGREGOR RANGE

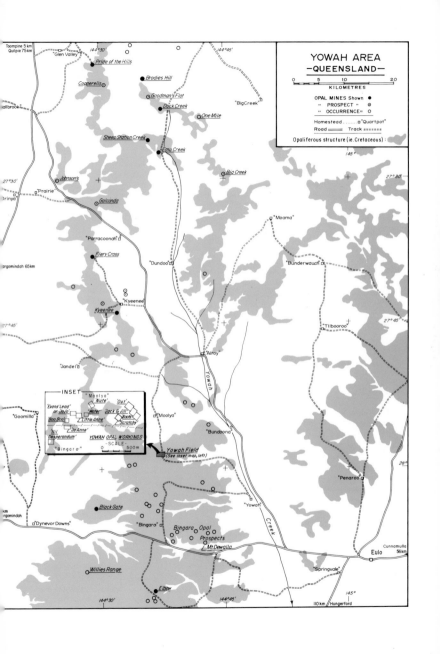

YOWAH AREA
—QUEENSLAND—

KILOMETRES
0   5   10   20

OPAL MINES Shown ●
   "   PROSPECT " ◉
   "   OCCURRENCE" ○

Homestead........□ "Quartpot"
Road ═══════ Track ════════

Opaliferous structure (ie. Cretaceous):

INSET

"Moolya"
"Nute"
"Out"
'Evans'Lead'
or 'JoJo'
"Water" "Jack & Jill"
Boo Boo   "Boots"
"Little Anne" "Scratch"
'Nil
Desperandum' "Jo Anne"
"Bingara"
YOWAH OPAL WORKINGS
—SCALE—
0   500m

Toompine 5 km
Quilpie 75km
"Glen Valley"
144°30'   144°45'
●Pride of the Hills
Copperella ◉   "BigCreek"
●Brodies Hill
◉Goodman's Flat
allbrook   ●Duck Creek
                   ●One Mile
●Sheep Station Creek
●Emu Creek
                   Big Creek
27°30'   Johnson's   145°   27°30'
□ "Prairie"
Orinya
Golconda ◉
                              "Moama"
"Parracoonah" □
argomindah 65km ●Fiery Cross   "Bunderwaugh" □
                 "Dundoo" □
                                         "Tilbooroo" □
●● "Kyeenee"
27°45' Kyeenee ●   27°45'
"Jandel" □
                   "Alroy"
                    Yowah
"Moolya"
"Goomilla"   "Bundoona"
                                        28°
"Bingara"   Yowah Field
                   ■ (See inset map, left)
                                        "Penaroo" □
●Black Gate
"Dynevor Downs" □   "Bingara" □
rgomindah   Bingara Opal
km   Prospects
                         "Mt.Dewalla"   Cunnamulla
                                               Eulo 56km
●Willies Range   "Springvale" □
●Elbow
144°30'   144°45'   145°
                  110 km Hungerford

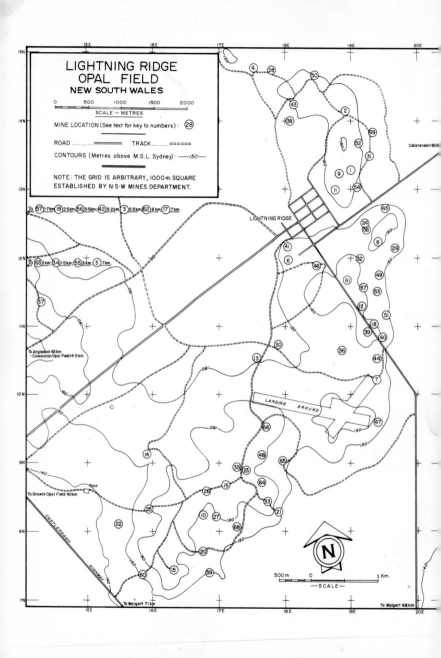

List of Mines at Lightning Ridge, New South Wales

1.	Angledool	36.	Mulga Rush
2.	Bald Hill	37.	Nebea
3.	Berlin Rush	38.	New Chum
4.	Bill the Boer	39.	New Dry Rush
5.	Bishop's Rush	40.	New Nobby
6.	Bulloch's Head	41.	New Town
7.	Bullockies	42.	Nine Mile
8.	Butterfly	43.	Old Chum
9.	Campbell's Hill	44.	Old Nobby
10.	Canadas	45.	Old Town
11.	Canfells Hill	46.	Paddy Burke's
12.	Cleared Line	47.	Palestine
13.	Darbys	48.	Phil Herbert's Rush
14.	Deep Belars	49.	Pony Fence
15.	Deep 4-Mile	50.	Potch Point
16.	Deep 3-Mile	51.	Poverty Point
17.	Dentist Hill	52.	Pumpkin Flat
18.	Dry Rush	53.	The Rocker
19.	Foley's 6-Mile	54.	Round Hill
20.	Four Mile Flat	55.	Rouse's 6-Mile
21.	Frog Hollow	56.	Seven Mile
22.	Frying Pan	57.	Shearer's Rush
23.	The Gully	58.	Sims Hill
24.	Hatters	59.	Small Belars
25.	Hawkes Nest	60.	Snowy Brown's
26.	Hearts and Spices	61.	Telephone Line
27.	Holdens	62.	Ten Mile
28.	Hornet's Rush	63.	Thorley's 6-Mile
29.	Indian's Lookout	64.	Three Mile
30.	Jungle Workings	65.	Three Mile Flat
31.	Killing Yard	66.	Vertical Bill
32.	Kingfisher	67.	Walshe's
33.	Lunatic Hill	68.	Western Fall
34.	McDonald's 6-Mile	69.	The Yank
35.	McNamara's		

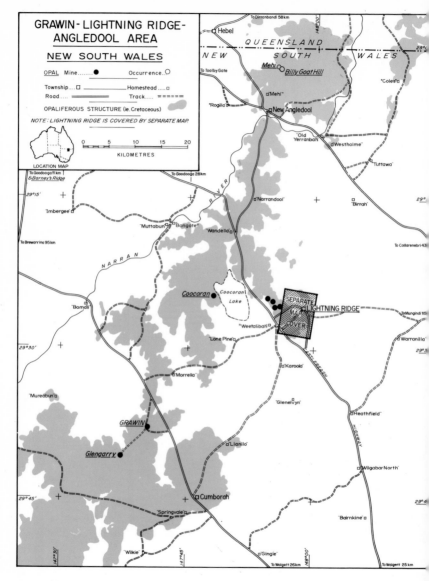

GRAWIN-LIGHTNING RIDGE-ANGLEDOOL AREA

NEW SOUTH WALES

OPAL Mine........●   Occurrence..○

Township....□ —————— Homestead .....□
Road..... ═══════════ Track..... ═ ═ ═ ═ ═

OPALIFEROUS STRUCTURE (ie.Cretaceous)

NOTE: LIGHTNING RIDGE IS COVERED BY SEPARATE MAP

LOCATION MAP

0   5   10   15   20
KILOMETRES

146

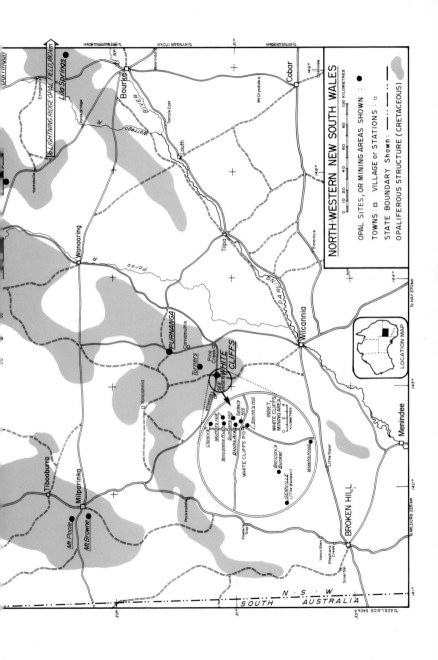

NORTH-WESTERN NEW SOUTH WALES

OPAL SITES, OR MINING AREAS SHOWN : •

TOWNS : □   VILLAGE or STATIONS : ▫

STATE BOUNDARY Shown : — · · — · · —

OPALIFEROUS STRUCTURE (CRETACEOUS)

0 10 20   40   60   80   100 KILOMETRES

LOCATION MAP

INSET
WHITE CLIFFS
MINING AREA
0   2   4   6
KILOMETRES

WHITE CLIFFS P.O.

GEMVILLE
(The Bunker)

Brueglok's
Bunker

Monte Kooba

Litle Topar

Smith's Hill

Turley's Hill

Sullivan's Hill

Blocks Area

Yancannia Rubbish Hill

Martin's Hill

Classen's Hill

Pine Creek

WHITE CLIFFS

SEE
INSET

Turners

PURNANGA

Carnmathie

Yancannia

Wilcannia

Tilpa

Wanaaring

Bourke

Cobar

Mt Drysdale

Yallville

Emmdale

Gundabooka

Louth

Thoolie East

Booroolloo

Fords Bridge

Engonnia

Yantabulla

Lila Springs

To LIGHTNING RIDGE OPAL FIELD, 180km

To BREWARRINA 80km

To BREWARRINA 80km

To NYNGAN 170km

To NYNGAN 95km

PAROO

DARLING RIVER

Warrego RIVER

To Mildura 225km

Tibooburra

Milparinka

Mt Poole

Mt Browne

Peckodilla

Fowlers Gap

Yanco Glen

Stephens Creek

Silverton

BROKEN HILL

To HAY 270km

To ADELAIDE 540km

N. S. W.

SOUTH   AUSTRALIA

Menindee

31°

30°

31°

31°

30°

146°

145°

144°

143°

142°

141°

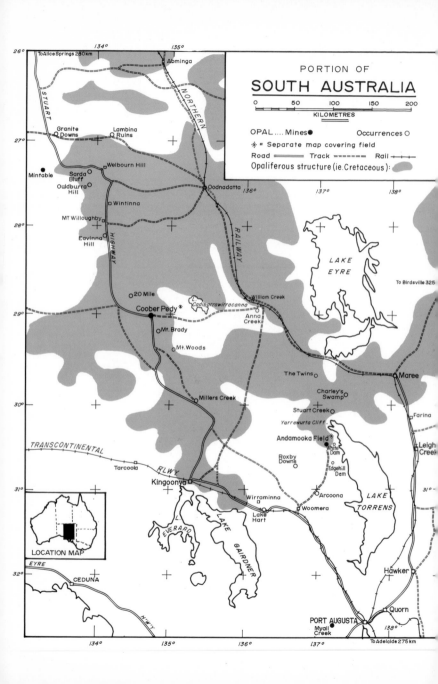

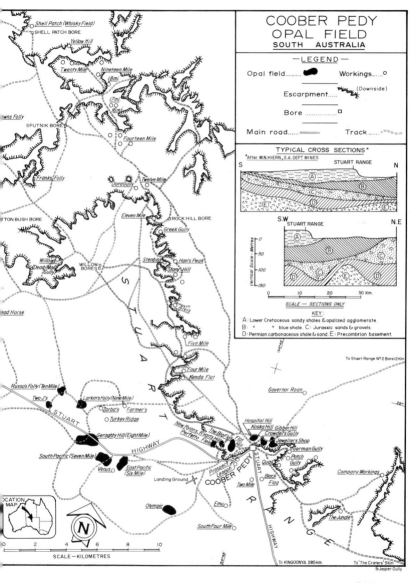

COOBER PEDY OPAL FIELD
SOUTH AUSTRALIA

—LEGEND—

Opal field........ ●   Workings......o

Escarpment..... ⌐⌐⌐⌐ (Downside)

Bore .... ▢

Main road..... ═══   Track...... ═══

TYPICAL CROSS SECTIONS
*After M.N.HIERN, S.A.DEPT. MINES

S   STUART RANGE   N

S.W   STUART RANGE   N.E

Vertical Scale—Metres

0

-100

-150

0   10   20   30 Km.

SCALE — SECTIONS ONLY

KEY:
A: Lower Cretaceous sandy shales & opalized agglomerate.
B: " " blue shale. C: Jurassic sands & gravels.
D: Permian carbonaceous shale & sand. E: Precambrian basement.

Shell Patch (Whisky Field)
SHELL PATCH BORE
Yellow Hill
Twenty Mile
Nineteen Mile
(18mi.)
owns Folly
SPUTNIK BORE
17mi.
16mi.
Fourteen Mile
Franks Folly
Dora Gully
Twelve Mile
TON BUSH BORE
Eleven Mile
ROCK HILL BORE
Greek Gully
Willows
Dead Man Gully
WILLOW BORES
Stenbiss
Han's Peak
Stony Hill
Elvis
Five Mile
Four Mile
Kenda Flat
To Stuart Range Nº2 Bore 12 Km.
Russo's Folly (Ten Mile)
Two J's
Larkin's Folly (Nine Mile)
Zorba's
Farmer's
Governor Roan
Turkey Ridge
STUART
Geraghty Hill (Eight Mile)
HIGHWAY
New Ryans
Ryans Hill
Perrero
Hospital Hill
Koska Hill
Gibber Hill
Crowder's Gully
Jeweller's Shop
German Gully
South Pacific (Seven Mile)
Venus
East Pacific (Six Mile)
Landing Ground
Prospect
Lennox
COOBER PEDY
Quail
Patch Gully
Black Flag
Company Workings
Two Mile
Olympic
Emu
South Four Mile
The Jungle
LOCATION MAP
STUART
RANGE
HIGHWAY
To The Craters 5Km.
& Jasper Gully
To KINGOONYA 285Km.

N

0   2   4   6   8   10
SCALE—KILOMETRES

dead Horse

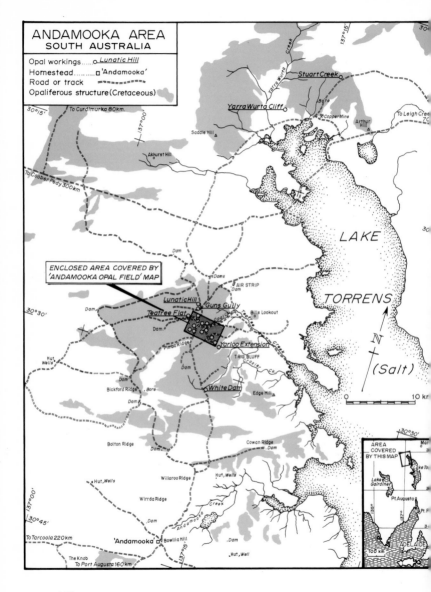

ANDAMOOKA AREA
SOUTH AUSTRALIA

Opal workings.....○ *Lunatic Hill*
Homestead..........□ *'Andamooka'*
Road or track ═══════
Opaliferous structure (Cretaceous)

To Curdimurka 80km.

To Leigh Creek

To Coober Pedy 300km.

Stuart Creek

Yarra Wurta Cliff○

Copper Mine

Arthur Hill

Saddle Hill

Akhurst Hill

Dam

Dams

LunaticHill

AIR STRIP

Guns Gully

Dam

Teatree Flat

Bills Lookout

Dam

Yarloo Extension

Pimba Ridge

TRIG BLUFF

Hut, Wells

LAKE

TORRENS

Dam

Bickford Ridge

Bore

Dam

White Dam

Edge Hill

N

(Salt)

0   10 km

Bolton Ridge

Dam

Cowan Ridge

Dam

Williaroo Ridge

Hut, Wells

Hut, Wells

Wirrda Ridge

Creek

Dam

To Tarcoola 220km.

'Andamooka' ▫ Bowilla Hill

Andamooka Creek

Dam

Hut, Well

The Knob
To Port Augusta 160km.

ENCLOSED AREA COVERED BY
'ANDAMOOKA OPAL FIELD' MAP

AREA
COVERED
BY THIS MAP

Lake Torrens

Lake
Gairdner

Pt. Augusta

ADELAIDE

100 km

150

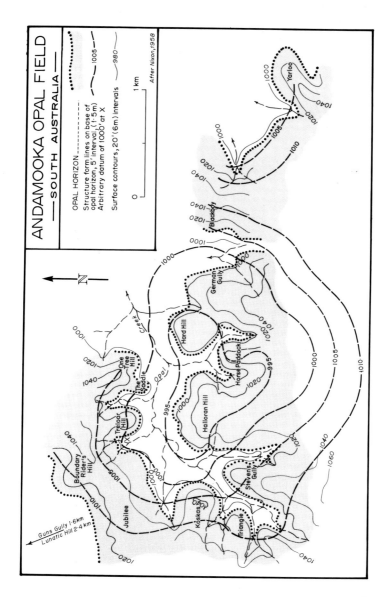

ANDAMOOKA OPAL FIELD
— SOUTH AUSTRALIA —

OPAL HORIZON ············
Structure form lines on base of
opal horizon, 5' interval, (1·5m)
Arbitrary datum of 1000' at X
———— 1005 ————

Surface contours, 20' (6m) intervals
———— 980 ————

After Nixon, 1958

0   1 km

N

Yarloo
1000
1040
1020
1005
1010

1000
1020
1040

1020
Blackboy
1040

1000
1000
German Gully
1000
1040
1020
Hard Hill
1020
Horse Paddock
995
1020
1000
Halloran Hill
One Tree Hill
The Saddle
Opal
Treloar Hill
1040
1020
1000
Boundary Riders Hill
Jubilee
1040
1010
Guns Gully 1·6km
Lunatic Hill 2·4km
1020
Koskas
Stevens Gully
Triangle
1040
1060
1010
1005
1000
995
Creek
1000
1040
1000
1020

INDEX

156